KU-731-166

MATHEMATICAL AND STATISTICAL TECHNIQUES
FOR INDUSTRY

MONOGRAPH NO. 1

MATHEMATICAL TREND CURVES: AN AID TO FORECASTING

MATHEMATICAL AND STATISTICAL TECHNIQUES
FOR INDUSTRY

MONOGRAPH NO. 1

MATHEMATICAL TREND CURVES: AN AID TO FORECASTING

J. V. GREGG, B.A.

C. H. HOSSELL, M.A.

J. T. RICHARDSON, B.Sc.

WITHDRAWN

Published for
IMPERIAL CHEMICAL INDUSTRIES LIMITED
by
OLIVER & BOYD

INSTITUTE OF ECONOMICS
AND STATISTICS
OXFORD. HA 297
47,356

OLIVER AND BOYD LTD.

Tweeddale Court
Edinburgh 1

39A Welbeck Street
London, W.1

These monographs were originally written as I.C.I. reports
for distribution within the Company, to meet a need for
simple expositions of modern mathematical techniques and
their application to practical problems. Each of them deals
with a particular technique which I.C.I. staff have helped to
develop, and which has proved to be of value to the
Company. In view of the widespread interest in these
methods, it has been decided to make these reports generally
available.

This edition first published .   .   . 1964

© 1964, Imperial Chemical Industries Limited

Printed in Great Britain by
Oliver and Boyd Ltd., Edinburgh

FOREWORD

This monograph has been written by a small team of people in ICI who have made a close study of mathematical trend curves and their value in long-term forecasting. It is one of a number prepared for the Statistical Methods Panel of ICI, which was set up to collate and disseminate mathematical statistical techniques of value in dealing with various problems, including those met in the techno-commercial and administrative fields. It is intended to publish further monographs on the application of such techniques.

Forecasting is indispensable in commercial and manufacturing activities, and forecasts are essentially subjective judgments made on the basis of existing information. It is usual and prudent to adopt alternative procedures in assessing the future and then to compare their results. There are various ways of basing forecasts on data available for a series of years. The most common is to analyse the economic, technical and commercial factors which have influenced the past figures and then, on the basis of assumptions on how these factors will operate in the future, to build up the forecast. Another method is to graph past data and, by use of a suitable trend curve, to extrapolate the past growth into the future. In view of the use of such curves as an alternative method, it is surprising that relatively little appears to have been published on the types of curves which have found favour and, as far as is known, no attempt has been made objectively to decide what curve or curves are at least consistent with the known data for the past.

The authors have tried to remedy this deficiency by writing a comprehensive document on trend curves and suggesting a method which affords some discrimination when the choice of a trend curve is being considered.

The information in this monograph represents the best current advice on the subject available to the publishers and authors. It is issued on the understanding that neither the publishers nor the authors shall be responsible for the absolute correctness or sufficiency of any information or illustrated tables contained in it.

COMPUTER PROGRAMMES

Copies of any of the complete programmes referred to in this monograph can be obtained, free of charge, in either Algol or Mercury Auto-code, by application to

The Information Officer,
Digital Computer Section,
Imperial Chemical Industries Limited,
Wilton Works,
Middlesbrough,
Yorkshire,
ENGLAND.

giving the appropriate reference numbers.

I.C.I. Ltd. wish it to be known that the programmes described in this monograph may now have been revised in content or improved in programming technique. The latest version will be provided on request.

CONTENTS

I

INTRODUCTION

Forecasting the demand for finished products, and for the raw materials and services involved in their manufacture, is necessary for the adequate planning of production and for programmes of plant expansion. The design and erection of new plant frequently take a considerable time, so that forecasts must be made several years in advance. In chemical and many other processes manufacturing costs generally fall with increasing plant size, and under-estimation of demand may result in unnecessarily high manufacturing cost and difficulties in meeting requirements. Over-estimation of demand, however, may lead to excessive plant capacity and to losses resulting from high capital charges and overheads.

It is clear that the accuracy of forecasting is of great importance, and this monograph deals with one of the techniques available to the forecaster, the use of mathematical trend curves. These curves are used for forecasting in fields as diverse as sales, usage of natural resources and raw materials, and labour requirements.

For the purposes of this monograph it is useful to have a uniform terminology even though the words may not always be exact definitions. The term " demand " will be used to define the variable to be forecast whether for goods, for services, for materials or for labour, and " market " to define the field of demand.

Any forecast must take into account the many factors which affect supply and demand, such as the state of the general economy, the policy of the Government, and the characteristics of the particular market in the development of new products and of new uses for established products. Many of these factors are qualitative and difficult to express numerically, whereas a forecast is usually required in a quantitative form.

Market research, consumer surveys, economic and commercial intelligence provide information about the particular market at the time and for a short time to come, and it is possible to forecast with some confidence for one or two years ahead by evaluating the major factors and assuming that the effects of other factors can be neglected. Such an analysis is inevitably imperfect because it only takes into account those factors whose influence is foreseeable. The history of the market of any product over a period of time includes gains and losses of uses and of customers which could not have been anticipated. It is a fortunate fact that over a number of years the net effect of this ebb and flow frequently follows a regular pattern. When a forecast is required for more than two or three years ahead it is seldom possible to assess all the factors likely to affect demand, and a common method of making such a forecast is by the use of mathematical trend curves. These curves are used to establish the growth pattern in the past and to suggest, by extrapolation, the future demand if the growth pattern continues unchanged. The numerical forecast obtained in this manner can then be examined and amended in the light of those judgments which it is difficult to express quantitatively.

A

Trend curves have been in use for various purposes for a considerable time. The logistic curve was used by the Belgian mathematician Verhulst in 1838 as an expression of the law of population growth. Also, since Gompertz (1779-1865) belonged to the same period and was especially interested in actuarial problems, it seems likely that the Gompertz curve was first suggested for that purpose about the same time. One of the earliest references to the application of mathematical trend curves to economic data is a paper by Prescott (1922) in which the Gompertz curve was proposed. This was closely followed, however, in 1924 and again in 1925 by papers by Pearl, who favoured the logistic curve. Since the subject undoubtedly grew from the drawing of curves through data, on either uniform or semi-logarithmic graph paper, it goes without saying that the simpler polynomials and the exponential have also been frequently used. One paper of interest is that by Daeves, who proposed the logarithmic parabola.

At the present time there is no coherent body of experience on this subject. It is hoped that this monograph will lead to the publication of case studies where trend curves have been fitted. The use of electronic computers makes light work of the calculations needed to fit trend curves and though the method described here is for hand computation it is readily adaptable for use on electronic computers.

In presenting this memorandum the authors hope that it will promote the use of trend curves as one of the aids to forecasting and stimulate discussion of the techniques suggested. Further experience in the use of these techniques may well indicate some changes and additions.

2

CHOICE OF TREND CURVE

2.1. GENERAL

It often happens that the demand for some commodity over a period of years presents an overall picture of steady growth, although in some individual years a fall in demand may occur. When attempts are made to forecast demand in future years this picture suggests the device of drawing a smooth curve through the scattered points and extending this curve to later years. It is preferable not to rely on free-hand methods, and normally some more or less simple mathematical equation is fitted to the demand figures, usually by " the method of least squares ". The fitting of a mathematical curve implies two assumptions. The first assumption concerns the type of curve which is chosen to fit the demand figures. The second is that the chosen curve will, when extrapolated, represent the picture of future demand.

A mathematical trend curve is fitted to demand figures in three stages. Firstly, it is verified that some trend curve will fit the data, in the sense that it is reasonable to attribute deviations of the demand figures from the curve to random or very short-term factors. This is described in Section 2.2. Secondly, the type of curve which best represents the data is selected as described in Sections 2.3, 2.4, 2.5. Finally, the best fitting curve of this type is calculated as in Sections 3.3 and 3.4.

2.2. EXAMINATION OF NATURE OF MARKET AND ITS REPORTED DEMAND

2.2.1. The Continuity of a Market in the Past

The longer a particular form of growth has existed the more likely it is that this form of growth represents the future progress of the market. Figures covering as long a period as possible should be obtained, since over a short period there is often little to choose between certain curves though the results obtained by their extrapolation may differ considerably.

When figures purporting to be representative of the demand have been obtained, the continuity of the market and the reliability of the reported demand figures as estimates of the actual demand should be established. The following general principles may be applied in assessing the data obtained:

  i) Examine the outlets for the commodity or service and ascertain whether they are sufficiently similar to be considered as a uniform market. When there has been a major change in the outlets or when the major outlets are dissimilar it may be advisable to consider them separately, since their growth patterns may differ.

  ii) Check if any major use or major demand (representing more than 25 per cent. of the market) appeared or disappeared during the period.

iii) Check whether a competitor, substitute, or import became a significant factor during the period studied. If so, it may be unreasonable to postulate uniform market conditions for the period. In general, examine the market history for any evidence of a permanent change in market conditions.

iv) Whenever possible base the study on total national demand rather than on the sales of one individual firm. The demand for the firm's product can be assessed as a proportion of the total market.

v) Ascertain whether the figures reflect true demand and are not affected by a limiting factor such as available supply.

2.2.2. The Future Continuity of a Market

An appraisal of the market and its demand requires an appreciation of the technological and economic factors of the market and possible changes in the future. The forecaster should be familiar with these factors and be in a position to reject those which have no long-term significance, and to suggest amendments to the forecast for those which have long-term significance. There are two types of factor which frequently receive undue attention. Firstly, there is the factor which may be important in the short term only, such as hire-purchase restrictions or a temporary recession in trade. Secondly, there is the factor which in a particular case may be unique, but which represents a recurring feature, such as the gain or loss of some small end use or customer. Such gains or losses are always occurring, and there is generally no good reason for anticipating a particular future event and allowing for it.

2.2.3. Examination of the Demand Figures for Exceptional Years

When the examination of the market factors affecting the demand figures has been completed, the figures should be plotted on graph paper and a smoothed curve fitted by means of a moving average, as described in Section 3.1. The moving average approximates to the long-term growth, and any divergence of the actual demand figures from the moving average should be attributable to temporary causes. There may be periods when the divergence is exceptionally large and persists for a year or two, but it is sometimes possible to attribute it to a particular factor, such as changes in the level of general industrial activity. It may be possible to reduce the effect of large short-term fluctuations if an appropriate index of industrial activity is available to adjust the data. However, the fluctuation may be due to unusual conditions in a particular year, and conditions in that year should be investigated. It may be desirable to examine the previous year as well, since the rise or fall of demand in a particular year can be the result of conditions in the previous year, such as abnormal stocks. Should market conditions in a particular year prove to be abnormal, the demand figure for the year should be ignored in the analysis, but for convenience in computation, it can be replaced by a notional value equal to one-quarter of the sum of the demands in the two previous and the two subsequent years. When it is considered necessary to adjust the demand figures in this way, the moving average should be recalculated and a final examination of the data can then be made. Usually no further readjustment will be required, and the appropriate trend curve can then be chosen.

2.3. MOVING AVERAGE AND SLOPE

2.3.1. Moving Average

As implied above, the progress of a market is seldom steady, and usually it is observed as in Figure 1 that in some years the demand differs substantially from the general progress.

Whilst it is evident that there is some form of progress, it is unwise to try to give greater precision to this intuitive concept by drawing a free-hand curve through the data. It is customary, therefore, to draw a curve by using a " Moving Average " technique to produce an approximation to the underlying progress in the market. When this has been done the magnitude of the fluctuation becomes more apparent.

FIGURE 1

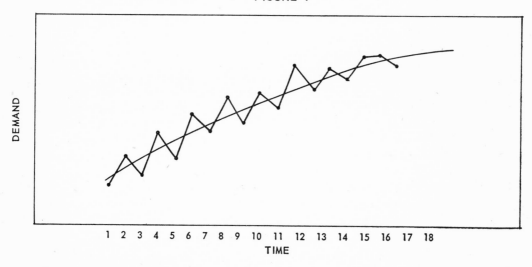

The " Moving Average " consist of a series of yearly plots each of which is essentially obtained as follows. Figure 2 shows part of the progress of the market shown in full in Figure 1. For illustrative purposes the time scale is increased. If a " best fitting line " PQ is fitted to the demand data, for example for the years 3 to 7, it will give an approximation

FIGURE 2

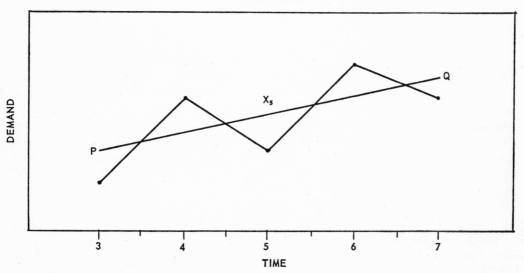

to the progress of the market during this limited period. Any point on it will give an estimate of the "average demand" at the appropriate time and, in particular, the mid-point of PQ (X_5) gives an estimate of the average demand at year 5, the mid-point of the period. By fitting similar lines to succeeding five-yearly periods, year 4 to year 8, year 5 to year 9, etc., a series of points X_5, X_6, X_7, ..., will be obtained, which give estimates of the average demands at years 5, 6, 7, ..., respectively. To obtain the appropriate values of X_5, X_6, X_7, it is not necessary to obtain the "best fitting line" in each instance. X_5 is equal to the average of the five yearly demands for years 3 to 7, X_6 the average of the yearly demands for years 4 to 8, etc. This is the reason for calling the plots X_5, X_6, X_7, moving averages, and the curve formed by these plots the "Moving Average".

The moving average produces a curve which reflects the underlying progress of the market but minimises the random fluctuation of the market about this growth. The longer the period of a moving average the more the fluctuation will be reduced and the smoother will be the curve formed by the moving average. As the length of the period is increased there is a tendency for the moving average to "iron out" the underlying progress, particularly when this is markedly non-linear.* It is prudent, therefore, to use as short a period as possible consistent with a reasonably smooth moving average. A moving average requires to be plotted at the mid-point of a period. It is, therefore, convenient to base it on an odd number of years since the mid-point of such a period coincides with an actual year.

2.3.2. Slope

The object of a forecast is to estimate the change from the current to the future position. When a trend curve is fitted to demand figures and extrapolated to provide a forecast, its reliability will be dependent on the accuracy of the slope of the trend. In Figure 2 the "best fitting line" PQ gives an estimate of the slope at year 5, the mid-point of the period. Similar estimates of the slope can be made for successive periods. If the trend is linear the estimates of the slope will be equal; if the trend is compound interest or modified exponential the estimates of the slope will be changing in a specified manner. The slope of the demand is, therefore, a criterion for the selection of the trend curve and forms the basis of the technique described in this monograph for choosing a curve. The word slope will be used to describe the series of estimates of the slope made at the mid-points of successive periods.

2.4. SLOPE CHARACTERISTIC

It is difficult to establish by inspection whether a particular mathematical form of curve can fit the demand data, though a gross misfit can usually be detected. To overcome this difficulty without the introduction of advanced analysis, a method of transforming the original demand data has been devised which should produce a linear relationship with time when the particular curve is able to fit the data. The transformations yield functions of the slope or rate of growth of the various trend curves which give straight lines when plotted against time. These transformations, called "Slope Characteristics", are applied to the demand data and the results are plotted against time. The slope characteristic for each trend curve is compared with the slope characteristic of the demand data and if the same linear relationship

---

* There are other methods using varying weights (see Appendix B of Monograph No. 2, *Short-Term Forecasting*). They are preferable in certain circumstances, but a little troublesome without the use of a computer.

with time is obtained for a period of the data then the procedure would suggest that there is no apparent misfit to the demand data for that period. If there is no similarity between the slope characteristics of the demand data and of the trend curve the procedure suggests that it would be inadvisable to use that trend curve for forecasting.

Such a system offers a method of studying how well the various curves can represent the given data, and hence of guiding the choice of curve to be used. So far as the authors are aware the technique is new, and, therefore, practical experience of its use over a wide range of examples is not available. It has, however, been used on data for chemical products, and for the majority of these the curve which best fitted the data was indicated. The authors consider that the technique is distinctly promising and its use can be recommended, but only by applying it in a large number of investigations can its value be fully appraised. In some investigations the delay resulting from extra calculations may be unnecessary where the form of the trend curve may be indicated by other evidence. It may eventually be concluded that there is no need to investigate the slope characteristics, but the procedures for fitting the various types of curves described in Sections 3.3. and 3.4. are unaffected. The technique is discussed more fully in Appendix 3.

2.5. VARIOUS MATHEMATICAL TREND CURVES AND THEIR SLOPE CHARACTERISTICS

The more commonly used trend curves can be grouped under three headings:

Polynomials
Exponentials
Modified Exponentials.

They are described overleaf, and a worked example for each type of curve is given in Sections 3.3 and 3.4.

[2.5.1. Polynomials

2.5.1. *Polynomials*

Straight Line: Demand $= a+bt$ where a and b are constants.

The slope of a straight line is constant, implying that demand is increasing by a constant amount each year; if the slope is plotted against time a horizontal straight line is obtained and this is the required slope characteristic. Figure 3 shows an example for which the growth can be adequately represented by a straight line.

FIGURE 3 – STRAIGHT LINE

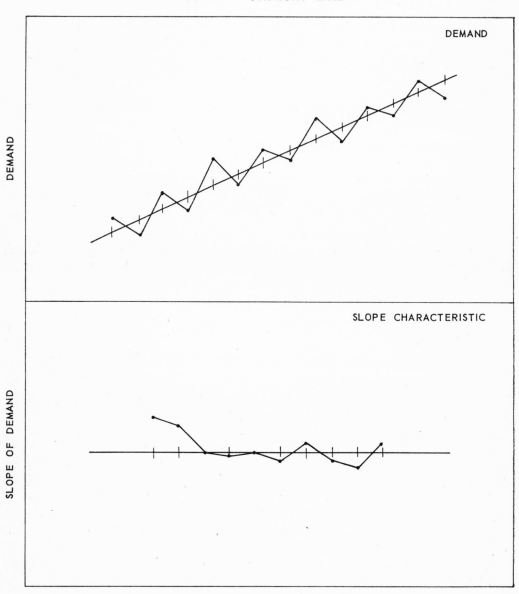

Parabola: Demand $= a+bt+ct^2$ where a, b and c are constants.

The slope of a parabola changes uniformly with time, and if the slope is plotted against time a straight line at an angle to the horizontal is obtained, which is the slope characteristic.

Figure 4 shows an example for which the growth can be adequately represented by a parabola.

FIGURE 4 – PARABOLA

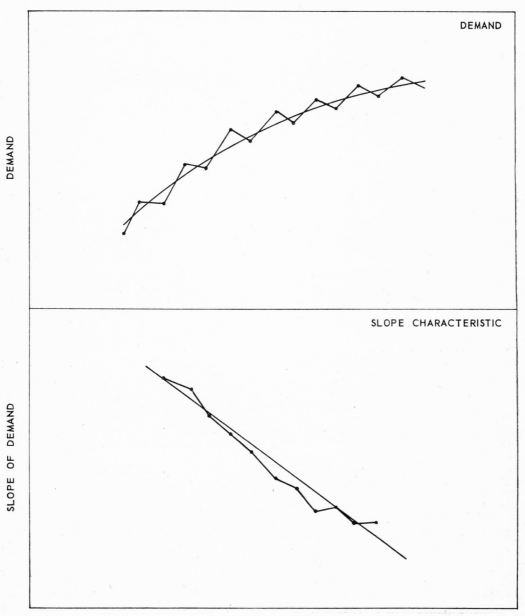

2.5.2. Exponentials

Simple Exponential: * Log (demand) $= a + bt$ where a and b are constants.

For a simple exponential trend curve the demand increases by a constant proportion each year, and the ratio of the slope of the demand to the demand itself is constant. The moving average gives an estimate of the demand and hence if the ratio of the slope to the moving average is plotted against time, a horizontal straight line will be obtained which is the slope characteristic. Figure 5 shows an example for which the growth can be adequately represented by a simple exponential.

* The simple exponential is sometimes referred to as the " Compound Interest Trend ".

FIGURE 5 – SIMPLE EXPONENTIAL

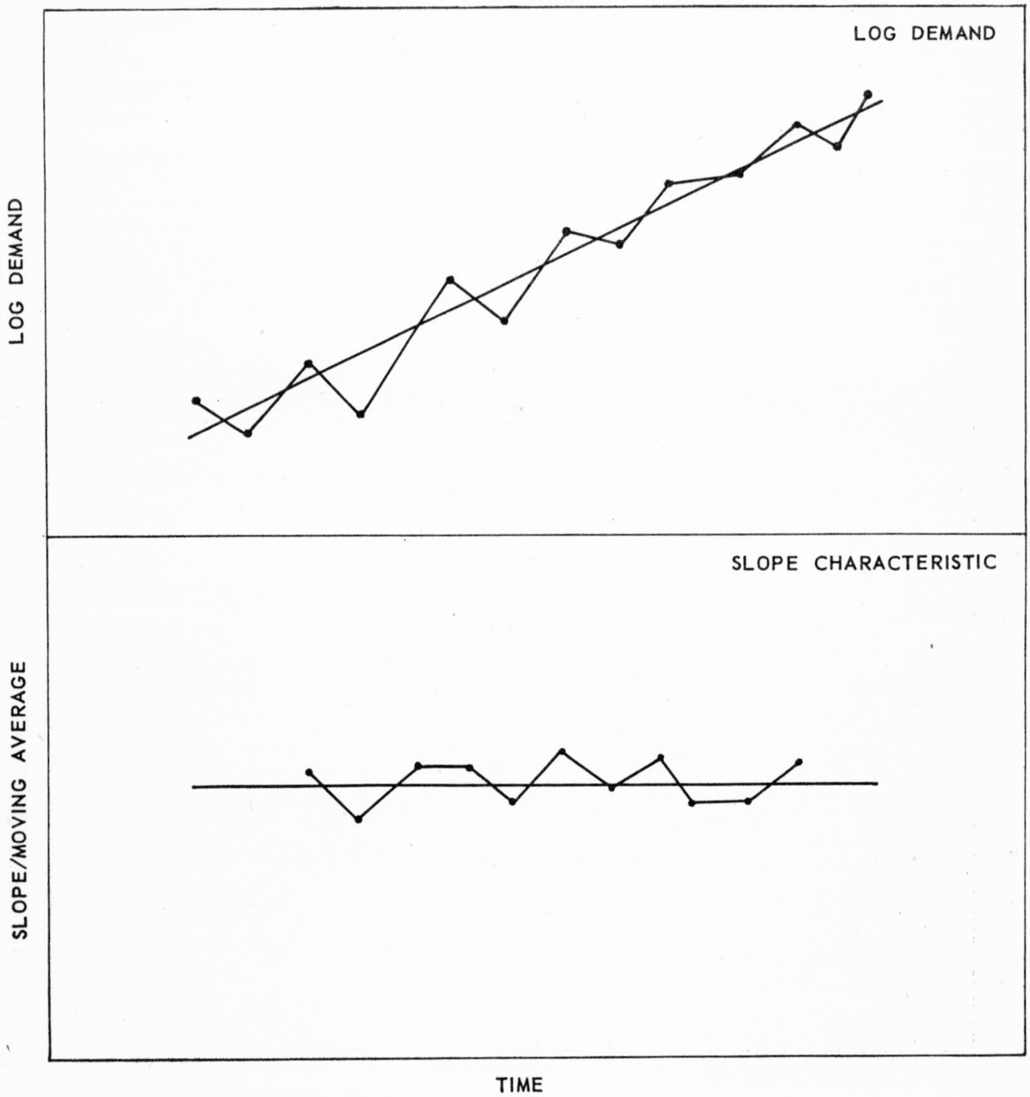

Logarithmic Parabola: Log (demand) $= a + bt + ct^2$ where a, b and c are constants.

While the ratio of the slope of the demand to the demand remains constant for a simple exponential trend, it varies linearly with time for a logarithmic parabola. If the ratio of the slope of the demand to the moving average is plotted against time, a sloping straight line will be obtained as the slope characteristic.

Figure 6 shows an example for which the growth can be adequately represented by a logarithmic parabola.

FIGURE 6 – LOGARITHMIC PARABOLA

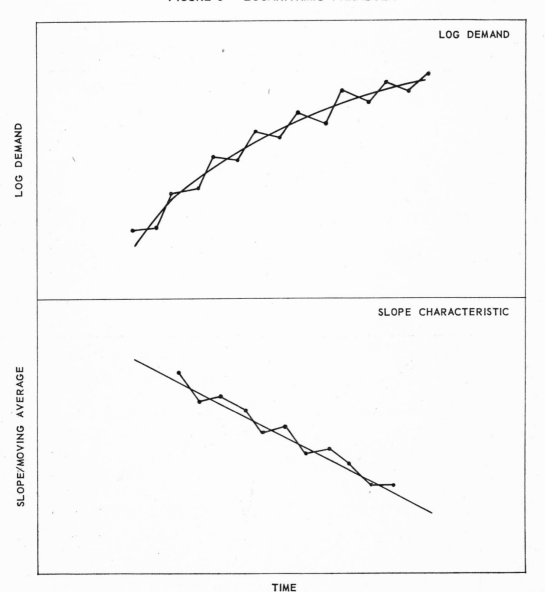

2.5.3. Modified Exponentials

The use of modified exponential trend curves implies the existence of an upper limit to demand which is approached asymptotically. The three commonly used forms are considered below:

Simple Modified Exponential: Demand $= a - br^t$ where a, b and r are positive constants and r is less than 1.

For the simple modified exponential, the logarithm of the slope when plotted against time gives a straight line sloping down to the right which is the slope characteristic.

Figure 7 shows an example for which the growth can be adequately represented by a simple modified exponential.

FIGURE 7 – SIMPLE MODIFIED EXPONENTIAL

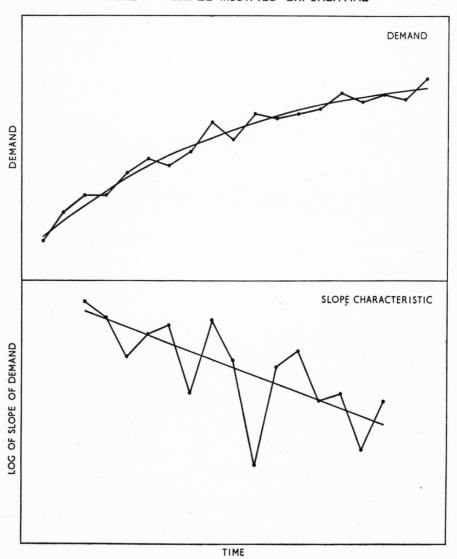

Gompertz: Log (demand) $= a - br^t$ where a, b and r are positive constants and r is less than 1.

For the Gompertz, the logarithm of the ratio of the slope to the moving average when plotted against time gives a straight line sloping down to the right, which is the slope characteristic.

Figure 8 shows an example for which the growth can be adequately represented by a Gompertz curve.

FIGURE 8 – GOMPERTZ

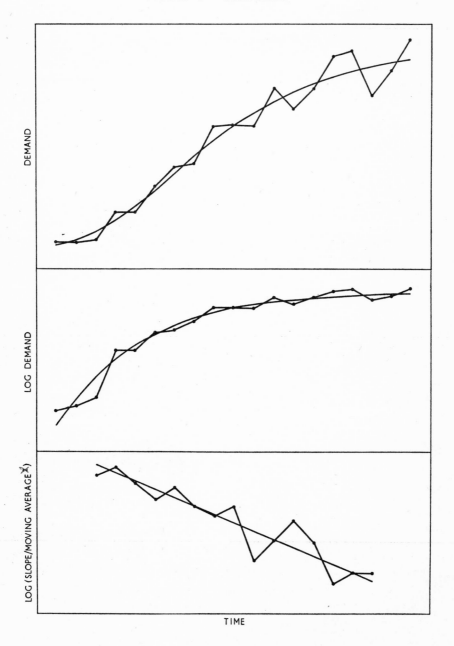

Logistic: Demand $= 1/(a+br^t)$ where a, b and r are positive constants and r is less than 1.

For the Logistic curve the logarithm of the ratio of the slope to the square of the moving average, when plotted against time, will give a straight line sloping down to the right, and this is the slope characteristic.

Figure 9 shows an example for which the growth is adequately represented by a Logistic curve.

FIGURE 9 – LOGISTIC

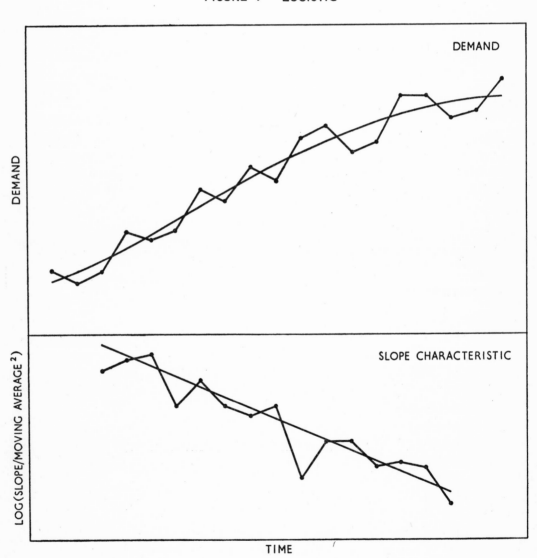

2.6. PROCEDURE FOR THE USE OF SLOPE CHARACTERISTICS

The various slope characteristics illustrated in the previous paragraphs have much in common and can be summarised as follows:

Compute and Plot Against Time	If the Result Oscillates about a Straight Line Which is:−	Then the Curve Suggested is:−
Slope	Horizontal	Straight Line
Slope	At an angle to the horizontal	Parabola
Slope/(Moving Average)	Horizontal	Simple Exponential
Slope/(Moving Average)	At an angle to the horizontal	Logarithmic Parabola
Logarithm of Slope	Sloping down to the right	Simple Modified Exponential
Logarithm of $\left\{\text{Slope/(Moving Average)}\right\}$	Sloping down to the right	Gompertz
Logarithm of $\left\{\text{Slope/(Moving Average)}^2\right\}$	Sloping down to the right	Logistic

Comparisons between demand data and the slope characteristics are best made by grouping in a manner similar to figures 3 to 9, but as follows:

Group 1

Demand data and moving averages on one graph.
Slopes of the demand data on another graph below.
Logarithms of the slopes of the demand data on another graph below.

Group 2

The logarithms of the demand data.
The ratios of the slopes to the moving averages on another graph below.
The logarithms of the ratios of the slopes to the moving averages on another graph below.

Group 3

The reciprocals of the demand data.
The logarithms of the ratios of the slopes to the squares of the moving averages on another graph below.

2.7. LIMITATIONS TO THE USE OF TREND CURVES

2.7.1. Data to be used for Fitting Curves

Even when the demand data have been examined as described in Section 2.2, it may be found that the slope characteristics indicate that a curve is consistent with the data only for a part of the period studied. Since this contradicts the basic assumption that the trend is a persistent relationship between demand and the passage of time, it is not legitimate to fit the curve to the whole data. It should be fitted only to that part of the data indicated as suitable by the slope characteristic, and since the curve is to be extrapolated into the future it is the most recent part of the data which must be used. If a curve is not consistent with the data for a substantial part of the total period, this curve should not be considered as suitable unless there are reasons for concluding that the market factors have changed in a way that is consistent with the changes in the graph of the slope characteristic for that curve.

2.7.2. Suitability of Chosen Curve

Although techniques have been described by which the suitability of the various curves for describing the data may be compared, it must be recognised that such methods can only guide the forecaster; they cannot replace judgment. The final decision on the most suitable curve to use still depends on the judgment of the user. Two important points must be borne in mind, viz.:

a) Markets can be divided into broad categories in which it is common to find particular types of curves, and it would be imprudent to choose a trend not customarily found. This is a point on which general guidance cannot be given. Experience and knowledge of a market are of considerable value; where such knowledge is not available, it may be possible to make use of the experience of others, for instance the opinions of those concerned in the movements of the corresponding American market.

b) Extrapolation of a trend should not give absurd results or results which cannot be supported by a general assessment of the market. Should the trend yield such results, the indications are that the curve used is merely smoothing the data and does not represent the rate of growth of the market.

2.7.3. Errors of Prediction

In the use of trend curves for forecasting, errors of prediction can arise from one or more of the following causes:

i) The trend may not in the future continue to follow the kind of curve chosen; for example, a point of inflexion may occur whereas the chosen curve contains no point of inflexion.

ii) The parameters of the curve have been derived from a limited amount of data and they will be subject to some uncertainty, which will lead to uncertainty in the position of the curve.

iii) The variation of the individual points about the fitted curve.

It is likely that uncertainty arising from cause (i) will increase as the period of prediction is increased, but it is not readily possible to give a quantitative expression to this uncertainty and particular caution should be exercised when predicting beyond five years.

2.7.4. Confidence Limits

The effects of uncertainty of prediction from cause (ii) of Section 2.7.3 can be assessed statistically. A convenient way of expressing the uncertainty is to state limits which, with a given probability, will include the true value; it may then be stated that the true value is unlikely to lie outside the limits given. Such limits are known as Confidence Limits and methods for their calculation are given in Section 3.7. The probability adopted in this report is 90 per cent. Thus, if limits are calculated as described in Section 3.7 it may be stated with 90 per cent. confidence that they will include the true value, provided the form of development of the market does not change markedly in the intervening period.

It is essential to recognise that these confidence limits give a range of uncertainty arising only from the estimation of the curve, and make no allowance for the uncertainty in choice of curve. Hence any doubts about the suitability of the curve will tend to increase the uncertainty of the estimates.

The choice of 90 per cent. confidence limits instead of the 95 per cent. limits generally used in experimental work arises from the recognition that long-term forecasting is a hazardous operation and that few people will expect a high degree of precision. A balance has to be struck between reducing the risk of error in the forecast by accepting wider limits between which the true value will lie, with the attendant risk of investing capital in idle plant, and increasing the risk of error in the forecast by accepting narrower limits with the risk of failing to meet demand. Ninety per cent. confidence limits seem to provide a reasonable balance between these risks and are, therefore, adopted here.

2.7.5. Variation of Individual Values about a Trend Curve

When a trend curve is fitted to a set of data, the individual values will not in general fall on the curve. The variations usually arise from causes which would be difficult or time-consuming to investigate, the recognition of which would not as a rule lead to much improvement in prediction. The value, for any year, predicted from the fitted curve is accepted as the most likely value of the demand in that year, and the confidence limits described in the previous section are the limits within which the trend value is expected to lie, when allowance is made for the uncertainty of estimation. This is the information usually required, but there are times when the individual values to be expected are needed rather than the trend values. For example, a commodity may be very valuable or difficult to store, and it may, therefore, be advisable to build a plant capable of meeting any demand likely to occur in a year. The confidence limits must then be widened to allow for the additional variation of the individual figures about the fitted curve. It would be possible to give tables which could be used in the calculation of these limits, but this would lead to confusion with the tables of confidence limits already given in this report. The alternative is, therefore, adopted of describing in Section 3.7 how these limits may be derived from the confidence limit tables which are given.

Before the confidence limits can be calculated, it is necessary to know how the individual values vary about the fitted curve. There is no general rule for this; for some markets the deviations appear to increase in proportion to the trend, while for others there is no evidence of such an increase. It is believed that most markets lie somewhere between these extremes. It is convenient and not unreasonable to assume that where an exponential curve is fitted the deviations tend to increase in proportion to increasing demand, and where a polynomial is used the deviations do not tend to increase. The confidence limits are then calculated in the same units as those used in fitting the curve; when polynomials are fitted absolute deviations are used, and since logarithms are used in fitting exponentials they are also used in calculating the confidence limits for the exponential curves.

B

3

FITTING TREND CURVES

3.1. CALCULATING THE MOVING AVERAGE AND THE SLOPE

3.1.1. Choice of Period and Method of Calculation

If a straight line is fitted to the demand data for a period of years the mid-point gives an estimate of the average demand, and the slope of the line gives an estimate of the slope of the progress of the market, at the middle of the period. If a series of lines are fitted successively a series of estimated average demands and slopes are obtained. The average demand values are known as the Moving Average. It is preferable to use an odd number of years as the period for the calculation, since the mid-point of the period, to which the moving average and slope correspond, will then be an actual year. It is generally desirable to use a period of at least five years. The estimate of the slope is subject to error depending on the length of period used and the variability of the demand data. If the period chosen is too short in relation to the variability of the demand data the estimated slope occasionally changes sign or becomes very small. In such circumstances it is necessary to use a longer period to calculate the slope for the Gompertz, Logistic and Simple Modified Exponentials.

The Moving Average is obtained by adding the yearly demands for the period and dividing by the number of years. For a five-year period the following calculations are required:

$$5 \text{ (Moving Average at year } t) = y_{t-2}+y_{t-1}+y_t+y_{t+1}+y_{t+2}$$

$$10 \text{ (Slope at year } t) = -2y_{t-2}-y_{t-1}+y_{t+1}+2y_{t+2}$$

where y_t is the demand in year t, y_{t-1} the demand in year $t-1$, etc.

For a seven-year period:

$$7 \text{ (Moving Average at year } t) = y_{t-3}+y_{t-2}+y_{t-1}+y_t+y_{t+1}+y_{t+2}+y_{t+3}$$

$$28 \text{ (Slope at year } t) = -3y_{t-3}-2y_{t-2}-y_{t-1}+y_{t+1}+2y_{t+2}+3y_{t+3}$$

In general for a $(2p+1)$ year period:

$$(2p+1) \text{ (Moving Average at year } t) = y_{t-p}+\dots+y_{t-1}+y_t+y_{t+1}+\dots+y_{t+p}$$

$$\tfrac{1}{3}p(p+1)(2p+1) \text{ (Slope at year } t) = -py_{t-p}-\dots-y_{t-1}+y_{t+1}+\dots+py_{t+p}.$$

The repeated application of these formulae is shown in Sections 3.1.2 and 3.1.3 and alternative methods of estimating the slope are referred to in Appendix 1.

3.1.2. Computational Method for Calculating the Moving Average

The determination of the average demand by a separate calculation for each year would be laborious. Instead the following procedure is suggested as a method for carrying out the computations in a systematic manner.

Consider the computation of a five-yearly moving average as shown in Table 1. For purposes of numerical demonstration the demand data for Commodity A, a chemical product, are included in Table 1. The complete data are shown in Table A.

y_1, y_2, y_3...are successive yearly demands

S_1, S_2, S_3...are the cumulative demands, namely,

$$S_1 = y_1$$
$$S_2 = S_1 + y_2 = y_1 + y_2$$
$$S_3 = S_2 + y_3 = y_1 + y_2 + y_3$$
....

A_t is the five-yearly moving average at year t.

[Table 1

TABLE 1 – CALCULATION OF A FIVE-YEARLY MOVING AVERAGE

Demand Year	Demand	Cumulative Demand		5 × Moving Average	Moving Average Year
Col. 1	Col. 2	Col. 3	Col. 4	Col. 5	Col. 6
1	$y_1 = 5 \cdot 7$	$S_1 = y_1 = 5 \cdot 7$			
2	$y_2 = 6 \cdot 9$	$S_2 = S_1 + y_2 = 12 \cdot 6$			
3	$y_3 = 8 \cdot 5$	$S_3 = S_2 + y_3 = 21 \cdot 1$			
4	$y_4 = 9 \cdot 6$	$S_4 = S_3 + y_4 = 30 \cdot 7$			
5	$y_5 = 11 \cdot 6$	$S_5 = S_4 + y_5 = 42 \cdot 3$		$5A_3 = S_5 = 42 \cdot 3$	3
6	$y_6 = 14 \cdot 1$	$S_6 = S_5 + y_6 = 56 \cdot 4$	$S_1 = 5 \cdot 7$	$5A_4 = S_6 - S_1 = 50 \cdot 7$	4
7	$y_7 = 12 \cdot 4$	$S_7 = S_6 + y_7 = 68 \cdot 8$	$S_2 = 12 \cdot 6$	$5A_5 = S_7 - S_2 = 56 \cdot 2$	5
8	$y_8 = 16 \cdot 0$	$S_8 = S_7 + y_8 = 84 \cdot 8$	$S_3 = 21 \cdot 1$	$5A_6 = S_8 - S_3 = 63 \cdot 7$	6
. . .	. . .	. . .	. . .	. . .	. . .
. . .	. . .	. . .	. . .	. . .	. . .
. . .	. . .	. . .	. . .	. . .	. . .
t	y_t	$S_t = S_{t-1} + y_t$	S_{t-5}	$5A_{t-2} = S_t - S_{t-5}$	$t - 2$
. . .	. . .	. . .	. . .	. . .	. . .
. . .	. . .	. . .	. . .	. . .	. . .
. . .	. . .	. . .	. . .	. . .	. . .
17	$y_{17} = 68 \cdot 5$	$S_{17} = S_{16} + y_{17} = 491 \cdot 4$	$S_{12} = 203 \cdot 7$	$5A_{15} = S_{17} - S_{12} = 287 \cdot 7$	15
18	$y_{18} = 71 \cdot 5$	$S_{18} = S_{17} + y_{18} = 562 \cdot 9$	$S_{13} = 255 \cdot 1$	$5A_{16} = S_{18} - S_{13} = 307 \cdot 8$	16
19	$y_{19} = 71 \cdot 1$	$S_{19} = S_{18} + y_{19} = 634 \cdot 0$	$S_{14} = 306 \cdot 1$	$5A_{17} = S_{19} - S_{14} = 327 \cdot 9$	17
20	$y_{20} = 80 \cdot 1$	$S_{20} = S_{19} + y_{20} = 714 \cdot 1$	$S_{15} = 359 \cdot 1$	$5A_{18} = S_{20} - S_{15} = 355 \cdot 0$	18
21	$y_{21} = 72 \cdot 9$	$S_{21} = S_{20} + y_{21} = 787 \cdot 0$	$S_{16} = 422 \cdot 9$	$5A_{19} = S_{21} - S_{16} = 364 \cdot 1$	19
Totals	$787 \cdot 0$			$3119 \cdot 3$	
Checks (a) $S_{21} = 787 \cdot 0$				(b) $\begin{matrix} 3189 \cdot 4 \\ 70 \cdot 1 \\ \hline 3119 \cdot 3 \end{matrix}$	

Checks

    a) The final entry in Col. 3 should equal the sum of all the entries in Col. 2. If it does not, recalculate Col. 3.

    b) The sum of all the entries in Col. 5 must equal the sum of the last (5) minus the first $(5-1)$ entries in Col. 3.

The steps in the above calculation are as follows:

i) Insert in Col. 3 the cumulative demand of Col. 2.

ii) Starting opposite year (5+1) enter Col. 3 in Col. 4.

iii) The entries in Col. 5 are five times the moving average. The first entry is opposite year 5 and each entry is equal to the entry in Col. 3 minus the corresponding entry in Col. 4.

iv) Starting opposite the first entry in Col. 5 enter in Col. 6 the series of integers starting with $\frac{1}{2}(5+1) = 3$. These give the years corresponding to the figures in Col. 5.

The above procedure can be generalised for any odd number of years. If, for instance, a seven-year moving average is required, then:

for ii) Starting opposite year (7+1) enter Col. 3 in Col. 4,

for iii) The entries in Col. 5 are seven times the moving average. The first entry is opposite year 7 and each entry is equal to the entry in Col. 3 minus the corresponding entry in Col. 4,

for iv) Starting opposite the first entry in Col. 5 enter in Col. 6 the series of integers starting with $\frac{1}{2}(7+1) = 4$. These give the years corresponding to the figures in Col. 5.

There is an alternative method for obtaining a moving average which can be found in statistical text books, but the method proposed above offers some slight advantages when it may be necessary to change the period for computing the moving average.

3.1.3. Computational Method for Calculating the Slopes

The direct computation of slopes by repeated straightforward application of the formula to each year separately can be tedious, particularly when it is necessary to use a period longer than five years. The computational labour can be lessened by using one of the following iterative formulae.

For a five-year period:

10 (Slope at year t) = 10 (Slope at year $t-1$) $+3y_{t+2}+2y_{t-3}-5$ (Moving average at year t)

For a seven-year period:

28 (Slope at year t) = 28 (Slope at year $(t-1)$) $+4y_{t+3}+3y_{t-4}-7$ (Moving average at year t).

For a nine-year period:

60 (Slope at year t) = 60 (Slope at year $(t-1)$) $+5y_{t+4}+4y_{t-5}-9$ (Moving average at year t)

and in general for a $(2p+1)$ year period:

$$\frac{1}{3}p(p+1)(2p+1)(\text{Slope at year } t) = \frac{1}{3}p(p+1)(2p+1)(\text{Slope at year } (t-1))$$
$$+(p+1)y_{t+p}+py_{t-p-1}$$
$$-(2p+1)(\text{Moving average at year } t)$$

The slope corresponding to the first period is calculated and the remaining slopes are then derived by the appropriate iterative formula given above. The layout for the calculation of the slopes is illustrated in Table 2 which is a continuation of Table 1. The symbol L_t is used to denote the slope at year t.

It is possible to check for arithmetical errors in estimating the slopes, as follows:

For a five-year period:

Sum of all estimated values of $10L$

$$= (2y_n + 3y_{n-1} + 3y_{n-2} + 2y_{n-3}) - (2y_4 + 3y_3 + 3y_2 + 2y_1)$$

where y_1 is the demand for the first year and y_n is the demand for the last year.

For a seven-year period:

Sum of all estimated values of $28L$

$$= (3y_n + 5y_{n-1} + 6y_{n-2} + 6y_{n-3} + 5y_{n-4} + 3y_{n-5}) - (3y_1 + 5y_2 + 6y_3 + 6y_4 + 5y_5 + 3y_6)$$

The coefficients required for the arithmetic check for the five- and seven-year periods can be rewritten as $(2, 3, 3, 2)$ and $(3, 5, 6, 6, 5, 3)$. The corresponding coefficients for longer periods of years are as follows:

> For nine-year period $(4, 7, 9, 10, 10, 9, 7, 4)$
>
> For eleven-year period $(5, 9, 12, 14, 15, 15, 14, 12, 9, 5)$
>
> For thirteen-year period $(6, 11, 15, 18, 20, 21, 21, 20, 18, 15, 11, 6)$, etc.

The computation of the slopes and checks is as follows:

TABLE 2 – CALCULATION OF THE SLOPE (5 YEAR PERIOD)

Demand Year	Demand	5 × Moving Average	Moving Average and Slope Year		10 × Slope
Col. 1	Col. 2	Col. 5	Col. 6	Col. 7	Col. 8
1	$y_1 = 5 \cdot 7$				
2	$y_2 = 6 \cdot 9$				
3	$y_3 = 8 \cdot 5$				
4	$y_4 = 9 \cdot 6$				
5	$y_5 = 11 \cdot 6$	$5A_3 = 42 \cdot 3$	3		$10L_3 = -2y_1 - y_2 + y_4 + 2y_5 = 14 \cdot 5$
6	$y_6 = 14 \cdot 1$	$5A_4 = 50 \cdot 7$	4	$y_1 = 5 \cdot 7$	$10L_4 = 10L_3 + 3y_6 + 2y_1 - 5A_4 = 17 \cdot 5$
7	$y_7 = 12 \cdot 4$	$5A_5 = 56 \cdot 2$	5	$y_2 = 6 \cdot 9$	$10L_5 = 10L_4 + 3y_7 + 2y_2 - 5A_5 = 12 \cdot 3$
t	y_t	$5A_{t-2}$	$t-2$	y_{t-5}	$10L_{t-2} = 10L_{t-3} + 3y_t + 2y_{t-5} - 5A_{t-2}$
18	$y_{18} = 71 \cdot 5$	...	...	...	...
19	$y_{19} = 71 \cdot 1$	...	...	...	...
20	$y_{20} = 80 \cdot 1$	...	...	...	...
21	$y_{21} = 72 \cdot 9$	$5A_{19} = 364 \cdot 1$	19	$y_{16} = 63 \cdot 8$	$10L_{19} = 10L_{18} + 3y_{21} + 2y_{16} - 5A_{19} = 17 \cdot 4$
Total					$665 \cdot 6$

Check that: $\quad 10L_3 + 10L_4 + 10L_5 + \ldots + 10L_{19} = (2y_{21} + 3y_{20} + 3y_{19} + 2y_{18})$

$$- (2y_4 + 3y_3 + 3y_2 + 2y_1) = 742 \cdot 4 - 76 \cdot 8 = 665 \cdot 6$$

The steps in the above calculation are as follows:

i) Starting at year $(5+1)$ enter in Col. 7 the entries in Col. 2.

ii) The first entry in Col. 8 is a direct estimate of the slope for year 3 based on the first five yearly demands. All subsequent estimates of the slope are obtained by using the iterative formula given in Section 3.1.3. $10L_4$ is equal to the previous slope $(10L_3)$ plus three times the corresponding entry in Col. 2 plus twice the corresponding entry in Col. 7 minus the entry in Col. 5.

This method can be generalised for estimating the slope based on any odd number of years. The generalisation is similar to that described in Section 3.1.2 for the moving average.

For a period of seven years:

i) Starting at year $(7+1)$ enter in Col. 7 the entries in Col. 2,

ii) The first entry in Col. 8 will be derived directly from the appropriate formula given in Section 3.1.1. All subsequent estimates of the slope are obtained by using the appropriate iterative formula given in Section 3.1.3 and the arithmetic accuracy is checked by the method given in that section.

3.2. EXAMINATION OF THE SLOPE CHARACTERISTICS

The calculations described in 3.1 provide the numerical basis for the examination of the slope characteristics of Commodity A.

3.2.1. Straight Line and Parabola

The appropriate slope characteristic is obtained by plotting the slope of the original data against time. For Commodity A these slopes are given in Table A, Col. 8, and are shown in Graph A2. The demand data and their moving average are shown in Graph A1, and it is clear that the trend is non-linear. This is confirmed by the slope characteristic in Graph A2 which rises to a peak at about year 9 to year 11, and then declines. If the trend of the demand had been linear there would have been no change in the general level of the slope characteristic.

The rise and fall in the slope characteristic indicate that a parabola cannot fit the entire period. From the years 10 to 21 there is a persistent fall, and an inspection of Graph A2 gives no indication that this fall is other than linear. Accordingly, the parabola is a possibility for the period years 10 to 21. The method for fitting the parabola is discussed in Section 3.3 and the calculations are shown in Table A.

3.2.2. Simple Modified Exponential

The appropriate slope characteristic is obtained by plotting the logarithm of the slope of the demand data against time. The slopes are given in Table A, Col. 9, for Commodity A, and are shown in Graph A3.

Examination of Graph A3 shows that the slope characteristic has a rise and fall. The modified exponential will not, therefore, fit the whole period, but as the slope characteristic is apparently linear in the period years 10 to 21 the simple modified exponential may fit this period.

The methods for fitting a modified exponential are discussed in Section 3.4 and Appendix 2. Two methods are described and the calculations for fitting the simple modified exponential using one of these methods are shown in Table A.

3.2.3. Simple Exponential and Log Parabola

The appropriate slope characteristic is obtained by plotting against time the ratio of the slope to the moving average.

The slope characteristic is given in Table A, Col. 10, and shown in Graph B2. The log demand is shown in Graph B1. Graph B1 is evidently non-linear, and without any indication from Graph B2, it can be stated that a simple exponential will not fit the data. The slope characteristic in Graph B2 again shows a rise and fall indicating that the log parabola could not fit the entire period. In the latter part of Graph B2 the fall in the characteristic is not markedly non-linear and the log parabola may fit this later period.

The method for fitting the log parabola is discussed in Section 3.3.3. The calculations for fitting the curve to the period years 10 to 21 are shown in Table B, Cols. 14 to 19.

3.2.4. Gompertz

The appropriate slope characteristic is obtained by plotting against time the logarithm of the ratio of the slope to the moving average. For Commodity A the required data are shown in Col. 11 of Table A and on Graph B3.

The slope characteristic shows a rise and fall indicating that the Gompertz cannot fit the entire period. The fall in the latter part of the period is apparently linear and the Gompertz may fit the data for this period.

The methods for fitting the Gompertz trend are discussed in Section 3.4 and Appendix 2. Two methods are described and the calculations for fitting the Gompertz to the period years 10 to 21 are shown in Table A, using one of these methods.

3.2.5. Logistic

The reciprocals of the demand data for Commodity A are shown in Table C, Col. 39. The slope characteristic for the logistic is shown in Table A, Col. 13, and consists of the logarithm of the ratio of the slope to the square of the moving average. The slope characteristic is shown in Graph C2. Graph C1 shows the reciprocals of the demand data.

An examination of the slope characteristic (Graph C2) indicates a general fall over the entire period but there appears to be a break in this fall during the period years 7 to 9. There is, therefore, some evidence that the logistic could not fit the entire period. When there is some doubt it is a safer policy to restrict the period since essentially the same trend would in any case be estimated from the shorter period. For this reason and to maintain comparability with the other suggested trends the logistic has been fitted to the period years 10 to 21.

The methods for fitting the logistic are discussed in Section 3.4 and Appendix 2. Two methods are described and the calculation for fitting the logistic using one of these methods is shown in Table C.

3.2.6. Remarks on the Slope Characteristics

There are some general aspects concerning the use of slope characteristics which may be of assistance in particular cases.

For Commodity A, Graph A2 shows a rise and fall. Such an occurrence means that the trend of demand has a point of inflexion where the slope ceases to increase; the curve is, therefore, S-shaped as can be seen from an examination of Graph A1. The occurrence of an S-shaped demand trend immediately debars the fitting of any of the following trends to the *entire* period:

> Straight Line
> Parabola
> Simple Exponential
> Logarithmic Parabola
> Simple Modified Exponential

If the logarithms of the demand data are plotted as, for instance, in Graph B1, the point of inflexion may disappear, i.e. the curve is no longer S-shaped. Only in such circumstances can the Gompertz trend fit the entire period. If the point of inflexion does not disappear then the Gompertz may still fit the demand data but only after the point of inflexion.

In a similar manner, if the reciprocals of the demand data are plotted, as in Graph C1, the point of inflexion may disappear. When the point of inflexion does disappear, then the logistic may fit the entire period. If the point of inflexion does not disappear, then the logistic may still fit the demand data but only after the point of inflexion.

3.3. FITTING POLYNOMIALS

3.3.1. Introduction

There are four commonly used polynomials which are fitted to demand data. Y denotes expected demand and t the year.

a)   i) Straight line $Y = a+bt$ ...(1)

      ii) Simple Exponential $\log Y = a+bt$ ...(2)

b)   i) Parabola $Y = a+bt+ct^2$ ...(3)

      ii) Log Parabola $\log Y = a+bt+ct^2$ ...(4)

where a, b and c are constants and $t = 1$ for year 1.

The values a, b and c are estimated by the least squares method given in the following sections.

3.3.2. Fitting the Straight Line and Simple Exponential

    Straight Line $Y = a+bt$ ...(1)

    Simple Exponential $\log Y = a+bt$ ...(2)

Let $y_1, y_2, ... y_n$ be the demands (or log demands for the Simple Exponential) for successive years 1, 2, ...n.

$$a = \frac{\Sigma y_t \Sigma t^2 - \Sigma t \Sigma t y_t}{n\Sigma t^2 - (\Sigma t)^2} \quad ...(1.1)$$

$$b = \frac{n\Sigma t y_t - \Sigma y_t \Sigma t}{n\Sigma t^2 - (\Sigma t)^2} \quad ...(1.2)$$

where Σ stands for the sum of all such items, from $t = 1$ to $t = n$, for example:

$$\Sigma t y_t = 1y_1 + 2y_2 + 3y_3 + ... + ny_n.$$

The formulae (1.1) and (1.2) can be used to estimate a and b but there is considerable computational effort and the opportunity for arithmetical error. However, they can be rewritten:

$$a = \frac{1}{M}(a_1 y_1 + a_2 y_2 + a_3 y_3 + \ldots + a_n y_n) \qquad \ldots(1.1.1)$$

$$b = \frac{1}{M}(b_1 y_1 + b_2 y_2 + b_3 y_3 + \ldots + b_n y_n) \qquad \ldots(1.2.1)$$

where the coefficients a_1, a_2, etc. and the divisor M are independent of y_1 to y_n and depend only on n. These coefficients have been tabulated for unbroken periods up to twenty years, in Table D.

To find the appropriate values of a and b for a straight line or simple exponential trend the following steps are required:

   i) Ascertain the number of years in the period.

   ii) Abstract the appropriate coefficients a_i and b_i and the divisor M from Table D.

   iii) Perform the computations indicated by formulae (1.1.1) and (1.2.1) above.

   iv) Use the estimated values of a and b in $Y = a + bt$ (or log $Y = a + bt$) to calculate the value of Y for each year taking $t = 1$ for the first year, $t = 2$ for the second year, etc. Continue estimating Y for further years beyond the period studied to provide the forecast trend.

   v) Plot the estimated values of Y against the corresponding years to show the trend and forecast.

3.3.3. Fitting the Parabola and Log Parabola

Parabola	$Y = a + bt + ct^2$	$\ldots(3)$
Log Parabola	$\log Y = a + bt + ct^2$	$\ldots(4)$

Let $y_1, y_2, \ldots y_n$, be the demands (or log demands for the Log Parabola) for successive years 1, 2, $\ldots n$.

As in the case of the linear trend, it is possible to estimate a, b, c, by the following formulae:

$$a = \frac{1}{M}(a_1 y_1 + a_2 y_2 + \ldots + a_n y_n) \qquad \ldots(3.1)$$

$$b = \frac{1}{M}(b_1 y_1 + b_2 y_2 + \ldots + b_n y_n) \qquad \ldots(3.2)$$

$$c = \frac{1}{M}(c_1 y_1 + c_2 y_2 + \ldots + c_n y_n) \qquad \ldots(3.3)$$

where the coefficients $a_1\ldots$, $b_1\ldots$, $c_1\ldots$, and the divisor M are independent of y_1 to y_n and depend only on n, the number of years in the period studied. These values have been tabulated for unbroken periods up to twenty years in Table E.

To find the appropriate values of a, b, c for a parabola or log parabola, the following steps are accordingly required:

   i) Ascertain the number of years in the period.

   ii) Abstract the appropriate coefficients a_i, b_i, c_i and the divisor M from Table E.

   iii) Perform the computations indicated by formulae (3.1), (3.2) and (3.3).

iv) Use the estimated values of a, b, c in $Y = a+bt+ct^2$ or $(\log Y = a+bt+ct^2)$ to calculate the value of Y for each year taking $t = 1$ for the first year, $t = 2$ for the second year, etc. Continue estimating Y for further years beyond the period studied to provide the forecast trend.

v) Plot the estimated values of Y against the corresponding years to show the trend and forecast.

3.3.4. Parabola fitted to Commodity A

An application of this method to the data of Commodity A is illustrated in Table A, Cols. 14 to 19.

The examination of the slope characteristics for the straight line and parabola indicated that the parabola was a possible fit for the years 10 to 21. This is a period of twelve years, and the appropriate coefficients for calculating the parabola for a twelve-year period are obtained from Table E. These are shown in Table A and in the extract from Table A given in Table 3 below:

TABLE 3 – CALCULATION OF PARABOLA

Year	Demand	a Factors		b Factors		c Factors	
Col. 1	Col. 2	Col. 14	Col. 15	Col. 16	Col. 17	Col. 18	Col. 19
10	23·8	3003		−869		55	
11	34·4	1911		−451		25	
12	42·5	1001		−111		1	
13	51·4	273		151		−17	
14	51·0	−273	$a = \dfrac{1}{4004}(3003\times23\cdot8 + 1911\times34\cdot4\ ....) = 16\cdot89$	335	$b = \dfrac{1}{4004}(-869\times23\cdot8 - 451\times34\cdot4\ ....) = 8\cdot98$	−29	$c = \dfrac{1}{4004}(55\times23\cdot8 + 25\times34\cdot4\ ....) = -0\cdot3367$
15	53·0	−637		441		−35	
16	63·8	−819		469		−35	
17	68·5	−819		419		−29	
18	71·5	−637		291		−17	
19	71·5	−273		85		1	
20	80·1	273		−199		25	
21	72·9	1001		−561		55	

The parabola is:
$$Y = a+bt+ct^2, \quad t = 1 \text{ for year 10.}$$

The value of a is found by multiplying each demand figure in Col. 2 by the appropriate a factor in Col. 14, adding, and dividing the result by 4,004. The values of b and c are found similarly. The parabola is therefore:

$$Y = 16\cdot89 + 8\cdot98t - 0\cdot3367t^2.$$

In a similar manner the log parabola is fitted as shown in Table B, Cols. 10 to 15.

3.3.5. Limiting Value of the Parabola

When a parabola or a log parabola has a positive b and negative c the form of the trend is an inverted U. In other words, there is a maximum or ceiling value for the demand. The ceiling value is equal to $(a-b^2/4c)$; it occurs at time $t = -b/2c$.

For Commodity A, the parabola has a maximum trend value of 76·8 occurring at $t = 13·3$ or year $13·3+9 = 22·3$, since $t = 1$ at year 10.

The log parabola indicates a maximum demand of 74·5 occurring at year 19·7. This suggests that the demand may have already passed its maximum.

The significance of these ceiling demands is discussed in Section 3.5.

3.4. FITTING MODIFIED EXPONENTIAL TRENDS

3.4.1. Introduction

As mentioned in Section 2.5.3 there are three commonly used modified exponential trends:

Simple Modified Exponential $\qquad Y = a - br^t$ $\qquad\qquad$ ...(5)

Gompertz $\qquad\qquad\qquad$ Log $Y = a - br^t$ $\qquad\qquad$ ...(6)

Logistic $\qquad\qquad\qquad\qquad Y = \dfrac{1}{a + br^t}$ $\qquad\qquad$ ...(7)

$$\text{or } 1/Y = a + br^t$$

where a, b and r are positive constants, r is less than 1 and $t = 1$ for year 1.

It will be appreciated that these trends are similar, the trend $a \pm br^t$ being fitted either to the actual demand, the logarithm of the demand or the reciprocal of the demand. There is, therefore, only one basic technique required.

3.4.2. Possible Methods for Fitting the Modified Exponentials

There are two methods in common use, of fitting a modified exponential:

 i) The three point method.

 ii) The Gomes method (least squares method).

The three point method is simplest but gives only an approximation to the best fitting trend. Where there is an observable cyclical fluctuation about the trend, such as a trade cycle, the three point method is best avoided. It does, however, provide a useful starting point and check on the more precise fitting obtained by the least squares method.

The Gomes method makes use of tables to give an exact solution. The extent of the existing tables is limited and they refer to unbroken time series. When the data for some years are missing it is necessary to use notional values for these years if the tables are to be employed. Computer programmes have been developed to do this calculation and to overcome the difficulties of giving each of the demand data its appropriate importance in the calculation.

3.4.3 First Approximation to the Simple Modified Exponential by the Three Point Method

The simple modified exponential is of the form:

$$Y = a - br^t \qquad\qquad ...(5)$$

and the three point method effectively provides three " average values " which should satisfy the equation. The standard method is to divide the period into three equal periods ignoring one or two years at the beginning of the period if necessary. The average demands for the three periods are found and these are used to determine a, b and r.

When the slope characteristic indicates that the demand is consistent with a modified exponential trend it is preferable to use estimates at the centre and near the beginning and end of the period chosen for fitting the modified exponential.

If the demand data are y_1, y_2, y_3, ...y_n the estimate of the average demand near the beginning is:

$$R = \tfrac{1}{5}(y_1 + y_2 + y_3 + y_4 + y_5) \qquad \qquad ...(5.1)$$

and near the end of the period:

$$T = \tfrac{1}{5}(y_n + y_{n-1} + y_{n-2} + y_{n-3} + y_{n-4}). \qquad \qquad ...(5.2)$$

The average demand in the middle is the average of the demand for the middle five years, when the total number of years is odd, or the middle six years when the total number of years is even. This average demand is denoted by S.

The determination of a, b, r is as follows:

$$r^{(n-5)/2} = \frac{T-S}{S-R} \text{ or } \text{Log } r = \frac{2}{n-5} \log \frac{T-S}{S-R} \qquad ...(5.3)$$

$$a = \frac{S^2 - TR}{2S - T - R} \qquad \qquad ...(5.4)$$

$$b = \frac{5}{(r + r^2 + r^3 + r^4 + r^5)} \frac{(S-R)^2}{2S - T - R} \qquad ...(5.5)$$

3.4.4. Simple Modified Exponential Fitted to Commodity A

In Table 4 the three point method is used to fit a simple modified exponential to the demand data of Commodity A. Table 4 is a reproduction of part of Table A, Cols. 20 to 25.

The general formula:

$$r^{(n-5)/2} = \frac{T-S}{S-R} \qquad \qquad ...(5.3)$$

becomes in this case:

$$r^{(12-5)/2} = \frac{72 \cdot 82 - 59 \cdot 87}{59 \cdot 87 - 40 \cdot 62} = 0 \cdot 67299$$

$$\text{or } \log r = \tfrac{2}{7} \log 0 \cdot 67299$$

$$\text{giving } r = 0 \cdot 8930$$

$$a = \frac{S^2 - TR}{2S - T - R} \qquad \qquad ...(5.4)$$

$$= \frac{59 \cdot 87^2 - 72 \cdot 82 \times 40 \cdot 62}{2 \times 59 \cdot 87 - 72 \cdot 82 - 40 \cdot 62}$$

$$= 99 \cdot 477$$

TABLE 4 – CALCULATION OF THE SIMPLE MODIFIED
EXPONENTIAL BY THE THREE POINT METHOD

Demand Year	Demand			
Col. 1	Col. 2	Col. 21	Col. 23	Col. 25
10	23·8	23·8		
11	34·4	34·4		
12	42·5	42·5		
13	51·4	51·4	51·4	
14	51·0	51·0	51·0	
15	53·0		53·0	
16	63·8		63·8	
17	68·5		68·5	68·5
18	71·5		71·5	71·5
19	71·1			71·1
20	80·1			80·1
21	72·9			72·9
Total		203·1	359·2	364·1
Divide by		5	6	5
		R = 40·62	S = 59·87	T = 72·82

$$b = \frac{5}{r+r^2+r^3+r^4+r^5} \frac{(S-R)^2}{2S-T-R} \qquad \qquad \text{...(5.5)}$$

$$= \frac{5}{3·6063} \frac{(59·87-40·62)^2}{2 \times 59·87-40·62-72·82}$$

$$= 81·603.$$

Corresponding computations for the Gompertz and Logistic trends are given in Tables B and C.

3.4.5. Fitting Modified Exponentials by the Gomes Method

The Gomes method of fitting modified exponentials involves the use of tables of so-called J functions whose derivation is given in Appendix 2. These J functions have been tabulated for values of r equal to 0·01, 0·02, ...0·98, etc., and for periods $n = 6, 7, 8, 9, 11, 13$. These are given in Tables H, K, L, M, N, P.

Starting with the estimate of r provided by the three point method, two values of r differing by 0·01 are found, such that

$$W = \Sigma y_t J_{n,t} \qquad \qquad \text{...(5.6)}$$

where Y_t, the demand in year t, is positive for one value of r and negative for the other. If the values of W for the two values are W_1 and W_2, and the lower value of r is r_1, then the estimate of r is given by:

$$r = r_1 + \frac{W_1}{W_1 - W_2} \times 0.01 \qquad \qquad ...(5.7)$$

Estimates of a and b can now be found:

$$a = \frac{\Sigma P_{n,t} y_t}{\Sigma P_{n,t}} = \frac{P_{n,1} y_1 + P_{n,2} y_2 + P_{n,3} y_3 + ... + P_{n,n} y_n}{P_{n,1} + P_{n,2} + ... + P_{n,n}} \qquad \qquad ...(5.8)$$

For odd values of n:

$$P_{n,n} = 1 + r^2 + r^4 + r^6 + ... + r^{n-3}. \qquad \qquad ...(5.8.1)$$

For even values of n:

$$P_{n,n} = 1 + r + r^2 + r^3 + r^4 + ... + r^{n-2}. \qquad \qquad (5.8.2)$$

Other values $P_{n,n-1}$, $P_{n,n-2}$, etc. are obtained as follows:

When n is odd:

$$P_{n,n-1} = P_{n,n} - r^{n-2}$$
$$P_{n,n-2} = P_{n,n-1} - r^{n-3}$$
$$...\qquad ...$$
$$...\qquad ...$$
$$...\qquad ...$$
$$P_{n,1} = P_{n,2} - 1 \qquad ...(5.8.3)$$

When n is even:

$$P_{n,n-1} = P_{n,n} - r^{n-1} - r^{n-2}$$
$$P_{n,n-2} = P_{n,n-1} - r^{n-2} - r^{n-3}$$
$$...\qquad ...$$
$$...\qquad ...$$
$$...\qquad ...$$
$$P_{n,1} = P_{n,2} - r - 1 \qquad ...(5.8.4)$$

The value of b is best given by:

$$b = \frac{1}{r} \frac{na - \Sigma y_t}{\Sigma r^{t-1}} \qquad \qquad ...(5.9)$$

This procedure, despite its apparent complexity, is well suited for calculation. An illustration is given in Section 3.4.6.

The available tables refer only to periods of $n = 6, 7, 8, 9, 11, 13$. If the periods studied are in excess of thirteen years it is necessary to divide the data into a number of equal groups. The number of groups should be a multiple of one of the available values of n. The modified exponential should first be fitted to averages of these groups. The modified exponential for the original data is then estimated as follows:

If $y_1 = A_1 - B_1 r_1^T$, where $T = 1$ for the first group average, is the modified exponential fitted to the grouped data then the modified exponential for the original data is:

$$y = a - br^T \text{ where } T = 1 \text{ for the first year, and}$$

$$a = A_1$$

$$r = r_1^{1/g}$$

$$b = \frac{g B_1 r^g}{r + r^2 + ... + r^g}$$

where g = number in group.

It will not always be possible to find a multiple of n to fit any given period, and then the demand data for a few of the initial years may have to be ignored. Further, in choosing the number in each group it is preferable to use the largest value of *n* available. If data covering eighteen years are available they should be grouped in nine pairs rather than six sets of three.

3.4.6. *Practical Example of Least Squares Fitting of a Modified Exponential*

The least squares method of fitting a modified exponential trend is illustrated below by fitting a simple modified exponential trend to Commodity A for the years 11 to 21. Because Gomes tables have not been calculated for a period of twelve years, it is not possible to estimate the trend for the period years 10 to 21 from the tables. The trend is fitted to the eleven-year period years 11 to 21 inclusive, using the *J* functions from Table N.

The approximate value of $r = 0.89$ has already been calculated by the three point method. It is, therefore, easily found that:

$$W = \Sigma y_t J_{n,\,t} \qquad \qquad \qquad ...(5.6)$$

is positive for $r = 0.88$ and negative for $r = 0.89$, as indicated in Table 5, in which the Gomes functions for $r = 0.88$ and 0.89 (obtained from the Gomes Tables) are shown.

TABLE 5 – LEAST SQUARES CALCULATION OF SIMPLE MODIFIED EXPONENTIAL TREND

Year	t	Demand y_t	$J_{11,t}$ $r = 0.88$	$J_{11,t}$ $r = 0.89$	r^{t-1}	$P_{11,t}$
Col. 1	Col. 2	Col. 3	Col. 4	Col. 5	Col. 6	Col. 7
11	1	34·4	+2,150·1	+2,418·5	1·0000*	−2·8310
12	2	42·5	+408·8	+508·8	0·8813	−1·8310
13	3	51·4	−689·3	−720·2	0·7767*	−0·9497
14	4	51·0	−1,273·4	−1,394·9	0·6845	−0·1730
15	5	53·0	−1,451·1	−1,622·6	0·6032*	0·5115
16	6	63·8	−1,311·5	−1,493·3	0·5316	1·1147
17	7	68·5	−928·3	−1,082·9	0·4685*	1·6463
18	8	71·5	−361·9	−454·8	0·4129	2·1148
19	9	71·1	+338·3	+338·2	0·3639*	2·5277
20	10	80·1	+1,131·9	+1,252·2	0·3207	2·8916
21	11	72·9	+1,986·4	+2,251·0	0·2826	3·2123

The sum of the products of Cols. 3 and 4 is 444·5 whilst that of Cols. 3 and 5 is −2,859·8. The least squares estimate of r lies, therefore, between $r = 0·88$ and $0·89$.

Interpolating between $r = 0·88$ and $0·89$ a better estimate of r is, from (5.7):

$$r = 0·88 + \frac{444·5}{444·5 + 2,859·8} \times 0·01 = 0·8813$$

In Col. 6 are shown the values of r^{t-1}, namely $1, 0·8813, (0·8813)^2$, etc.

To find a, the series of Factors $P_{11,\,t}$ are calculated. Since there is an odd number of years, namely eleven, from (5.8.1),

$$P_{11,\,11} = 1 + r^2 + r^4 + \ldots + r^{11-3}$$
$$= 1 + r^2 + r^4 + r^6 + r^8.$$

These powers of r are marked by an asterisk * in Col. 6, and $P_{11,\,11}$ is the last entry in Col. 7. Since the period has an odd number of years, other entries in Col. 7, $P_{11,\,10}$, etc. are obtained by successive subtraction of the entry in Col. 6 from the previous entry in Col. 7.

$P_{11,\,11} = 1 + (0·8813)^2 + \ldots + (0·8813)^8 = 3·2123$. Last entry in Col. 7.

$P_{11,\,10} = 3·2123 − 0·3207 = 2·8916$. Second last entry in Col. 7.

$P_{11,\,9}\ = 2·8916 − 0·3639 = 2·5277$. Third last entry in Col. 7.

$P_{11,\,8}\ = 2·5277 − 0·4129 = 2·1148$. Fourth last entry in Col. 7, etc.

When all the $P_{11,\,t}$ entries have been calculated, a is given by:

$$a = \frac{\Sigma P_{11,\,t} y_t}{\Sigma P_{11,\,t}} \qquad \ldots(5.8)$$

i.e. by adding the products of corresponding items in Col. 3 and Col. 7, and dividing the result by the total of Col. 7.

This gives $a = 94·1049$.

$$b = \frac{1}{r} \frac{na - \Sigma y_t}{\Sigma r^{t-1}} \qquad \ldots(5.9)$$

In this formula, a has been calculated, $n = 11$, the number of years in the period, and Σr^{t-1} is the total of the entries in Col. 6. Using these values it is found that:

$$b = 67·25$$

The least squares fit for the modified exponential is, therefore:

$$Y = 94·1049 − 67·25 \,(0·8813)^t \text{ where } t = 1 \text{ for year 11.}$$

3.5. GENERAL COMMENT ON POSSIBLE TRENDS FOR COMMODITY A

The application of the slope characteristic technique indicated that none of the specified trends would fit the demand data for the whole period, and that neither the linear nor simple exponential would fit the demand data for any substantial portion of the period. For the period years 10 to 21 any of the following trends appears to be possible:

Parabola; Log Parabola; Simple Modified Exponential; Gompertz; Logistic.

In Table 6 the various values for these five trends are shown for the period years 10 to 21 together with the extrapolated values for five and seven years ahead. The values for the modified exponentials calculated both by the three point method and by the least squares method are included.

c

TABLE 6 – COMPARISON OF DEMAND DATA AND TRENDS

Year	Demand	Parabola	Log Parabola	Simple Modified Exponential		Gompertz		Logistic	
				Three Point	Least Squares	Three Point	Least Squares	Three Point	Least Squares
1	5·7								
2	6·9								
3	8·5								
4	9·6								
5	11·6								
6	14·1								
7	12·4								
8	16·0								
9	18·2								
10	23·8	25·53	26·66	26·61		27·22		27·12	
11	34·4	33·50	32·64	34·40	34·84	33·83	35·22	33·04	35·14
12	42·5	40·79	39·09	41·37	41·87	40·39	41·61	39·34	41·34
13	51·4	47·41	45·80	47·58	48·07	46·67	47·67	45·72	47·48
14	51·0	53·36	52·47	53·14	53·54	52·51	53·23	51·90	53·28
15	53·0	58·63	58·80	58·09	58·35	57·81	58·24	57·61	58·50
16	63·8	63·23	64·46	62·52	62·60	62·53	62·65	62·66	63·03
17	68·5	67·15	69·11	66·48	66·34	66·66	66·49	66·96	66·82
18	71·5	70·41	72·51	70·01	69·64	70·24	69·79	70·51	69·90
19	71·1	72·99	74·37	73·16	72·54	73·29	72·60	73·37	72·35
20	80·1	74·89	74·63	75·98	75·11	75·88	74·96	75·61	74·24
21	72·9	76·12	73·27	78·49	77·36	78·06	76·94	77·35	75·70
Forecasts 26		72·2	47·9	87·6	85·2	84·6	82·8	81·4	79·0
28				90·0	87·2	85·9	83·9	81·9	79·5
Ceiling Demand				99·5	94·1	88·5	86·2	82·5	80·0
Root Mean Square Residual									
(i) Assuming variation stable.		3·4	3·8	3·6	3·6	3·7	3·6	3·8	3·6
(ii) Assuming variation increased proportionately with demand.		6·3%	8·1%	6·8%	5·9%	6·6%	5·6%	8·1%	6·1%

The root mean square residual (the standard deviation) gives an estimate of the average difference between the trend values and the actual demand, and gives the basis for the confidence limits which are discussed in Section 3.7. The root mean square residuals have been calculated by:

a) Squaring the differences between actual and corresponding trend values.

b) Adding these squares.

c) Dividing this sum by the total number of squares minus three.

d) Taking the square root.

Also shown are the root mean square residuals assuming that variation increases proportionately with demand.

It is generally possible to ascertain whether a decline in the growth rate of a market is due to the saturation of the market or to adverse technical factors. Where there is good reason to believe that the saturation point is near it is inadvisable to use a parabola or log parabola for forecasting, since either of these trends implies that if the growth rate declines it will continue to decline without limit. If, on the other hand, there is good reason to believe that adverse factors have been in action which could lead to a fall in the market, the use of a modified exponential trend is inadvisable.

3.6. ADJUSTMENT FOR GROWTH OF GENERAL ECONOMY

The use of modified exponentials when the demand is very near its ceiling and the growth rate is only of the order of 3 per cent. per annum can sometimes lead to biased forecasting. The modified exponential frequently reflects a rapid growth pattern of demand but it inherently assumes a fixed ceiling market. In an economy of fixed size this assumption is reasonable, but there is always a long-term growth in the economy as a whole which may effectively increase the ceiling market. If the demand is near its maximum and there is good reason to expect an expansion in its market owing to the growth of the economy, it will be appropriate to adjust the demand figures for the general growth. If the ceiling market were increasing at a rate of 2 per cent. compound interest the demand figures $y_1, y_2, y_3, ...y_n$, should be corrected to:

$$x_1 = y_1/(1 \cdot 02), \ x_2 = y_2/(1 \cdot 02)^2, \ ...x_n = y_n/(1 \cdot 02)^n.$$

The trend should be fitted to $x_1, x_2, ...x_n$. If this trend is a simple modified exponential, for example:

$$X_t = a - br^t$$

then the trend for the demand is:

$$\text{Demand} = X_t(1 \cdot 02)^t$$
$$= (a - br^t)(1 \cdot 02)^t.$$

3.7. CONFIDENCE LIMITS

3.7.1. Estimation of Confidence Limits

The confidence limits are based on the scatter of the points about the fitted curve; the greater the scatter the greater the uncertainty of the position of the curve and hence the wider the confidence limits. The first step in their derivation is the calculation of the standard deviation from the deviations of the points from the fitted curve. As the expected values over the period of the data will usually be calculated, the easiest way is to take the differences of these values from the corresponding values of the data and compute their standard deviation. This figure is then multiplied by a factor to give the amounts by which the confidence limits differ from the expected value for any given year; tables of the factors required for this step are given. Where the variation about the fitted curve is assumed proportional to the demand, as with the simple exponential, logarithmic parabola and Gompertz, the logarithms of actual and expected demands are used to obtain the deviations (see examples in Sections 3.7.3, 3.7.4 and 3.7.5.)

3.7.2. Confidence Limits for Straight Line and Parabola

In Section 3.5.2 it was pointed out that the equations of the straight line and the parabola were respectively:

$$Y = a + bt \qquad \qquad \text{...(1)}$$

and

$$Y = a + bt + ct^2. \qquad \qquad \text{...(2)}$$

The parameters a, b for the straight line, and a, b, c for the parabola, may be obtained by applying the formulae:

$$a = \frac{1}{M} \Sigma a_t y_t, \; b = \frac{1}{M} \Sigma b_t y_t \text{ for the straight line } (a_t, \, b_t, \, M \text{ from Table D}),$$

and

$$a = \frac{1}{M} \Sigma a_t y_t, \; b = \frac{1}{M} \Sigma b_t y_t, \; c = \frac{1}{M} \Sigma c_t y_t \text{ for the parabola } (a_t, \, b_t, \, c_t, \, M \text{ from Table E}).$$

When these formulae are used, the standard error of a forecast year " T " is:

for the straight line, $\sqrt{\Sigma(a_t + Tb_t)^2} \times$ standard deviation,

or for the parabola, $\sqrt{\Sigma(a_t + Tb_t + T^2 c_t)^2} \times$ standard deviation,

where the summation within the square root sign is with respect to t.

These formulae can be used directly to calculate the confidence limits of any prediction, by multiplication by a factor depending on the number of years for which data are used. Numerical values of the formulae have been derived for demand data for $n = 5$ to 20 years and for forecasts up to 15 years. To simplify calculation these have been combined with appropriate factors to give confidence limits directly, and are shown in Tables F and G and Graphs D and E.

The method of computing the confidence limits is thus as follows:

Compute the trend values using the appropriate formula

$$Y = a + bt$$
$$\text{or}$$
$$Y = a + bt + ct^2$$

for each year for which a figure is available for demand. Let these quantities be Y_1, Y_2, ... Y_n, the corresponding actual demands being y_1, y_2, ... y_n.

$$\text{Compute } S^2 = (Y_1 - y_1)^2 + (Y_2 - y_2)^2 + ... + (Y_n - y_n)^2.$$

Calculate the standard deviation

$$S/\sqrt{n-2} \text{ for the straight line or } S/\sqrt{n-3} \text{ for the parabola.}$$

Read the appropriate factor (say U) from Table F or Graph D if a straight line has been fitted, or from Table G or Graph E if a parabola has been fitted, and multiply this by the quantity above.

The 90 per cent. confidence limits of the predicted value for year "T" are then given by:

$$\text{C.L. } (T) = a+bT\pm US/\sqrt{n-2} \text{ for a straight line.}$$

$$\text{C.L. } (T) = a+bT+cT^2\pm US/\sqrt{n-3} \text{ for a parabola.}$$

Example

In Section 3.3.4 a parabola has been fitted to the figures for Commodity A for the years 10-21, the equation obtained being:

$$Y = 16\cdot89+8\cdot98\,t-0\cdot3367t^2(t = 1 \text{ for 10th year}).$$

The following table gives the actual demands, the figures derived from this equation, and the deviations of the latter from the former.

TABLE 7 – ESTIMATION OF

90% CONFIDENCE LIMITS FOR PARABOLA

Year	t	Actual Demand	Calculated Demand	Calculated – Actual
10	1	23·8	25·5	1·7
11	2	34·4	33·5	−0·9
12	3	42·5	40·8	−1·7
13	4	51·4	47·4	−4·0
14	5	51·0	53·4	2·4
15	6	53·0	58·6	5·6
16	7	63·8	63·3	−0·5
17	8	68·5	67·2	−1·3
18	9	71·5	70·4	−1·1
19	10	71·1	73·0	1·9
20	11	80·1	74·9	−5·2
21	12	72·9	76·2	3·3

$$S^2 = 104\cdot4$$

$$S^2/(n-3) = \frac{104\cdot4}{9} = 11\cdot6$$

$$S/\sqrt{n-3} = 3\cdot41.$$

The forecast demand for year 22 is obtained by substituting $t = 13$ in the equation, which gives 76·7.

From Table G for $n = 12$, year $(n+1)$ we obtain the factor 1·895.

Hence the 90 per cent. confidence limits are $76\cdot7\pm1\cdot895\times3\cdot41$, i.e. $76\cdot7\pm6\cdot46$ or 70·2, 83·2.

3.7.3. Confidence Limits for Simple Exponential and Logarithmic Parabola

As has already been explained in Section 3.3, the best fitting exponential is obtained by fitting a straight line to the logarithms of the original data; similarly the logarithmic parabola is estimated by fitting a parabola to the logarithms. The confidence limits for these two curves are derived similarly, i.e. the logarithms are used and the rules given in the previous section are applied.

Example

It has already been shown that a logarithmic parabola will give a reasonable fit to the data for Commodity A over the period year 10 to year 21. If these data are used, the equation obtained is:

$$\log Y = 1 \cdot 3284 + 0 \cdot 10231t - 0 \cdot 004805t^2.$$

The following table gives the logarithms of the actual demands, the figures derived from the above equation, and the deviations of the latter from the former.

TABLE 8 – ESTIMATION OF
90% CONFIDENCE LIMITS FOR LOGARITHMIC PARABOLA

Year	t	Actual Log Demand	Calculated Log Demand	Calculated Log − Actual Log
10	1	1·3766	1·4259	0·0493
11	2	1·5366	1·5138	−0·0228
12	3	1·6284	1·5921	−0·0363
13	4	1·7110	1·6608	−0·0502
14	5	1·7076	1·7198	0·0122
15	6	1·7243	1·7693	0·0450
16	7	1·8048	1·8091	0·0043
17	8	1·8357	1·8394	0·0037
18	9	1·8543	1·8600	0·0057
19	10	1·8519	1·8710	0·0191
20	11	1·9036	1·8724	−0·0312
21	12	1·8627	1·8642	0·0015

$$S^2 = 0 \cdot 01036707$$

$$S^2/(n-3) = 0 \cdot 00115190$$

$$S/\sqrt{n-3} = 0 \cdot 0339.$$

The forecast demand is obtained by the substitution of $t = 13$ in the equation to give 1·8464, and then taking the antilogarithm of this, which is 70·21.

From Table G, for $n = 12$, year $(n+1)$ we obtain the factor 1·895. Hence the *logarithms* of the confidence limits are:

$$1 \cdot 8464 \pm 1 \cdot 895 \times 0 \cdot 0339 = 1 \cdot 7822 \text{ and } 1 \cdot 9106$$

i.e. taking antilogarithms, the 90 per cent. confidence limits are: 60·6 and 81·40.

3.7.4. Confidence Limits for Modified Exponentials

It is possible to estimate confidence limits of extrapolated values of the simple modified exponential $Y = a - br^t$. Similar procedures using logarithms or reciprocals yield the confidence limits for the Gompertz and Logistic, respectively. The confidence limits required are the product of the standard deviation of the points about the fitted curve and a complex function of r and of n the number of years in the period.

The formula has been calculated for various values of r and n, and the results tabulated in Table Q. These tables give factors by which to multiply the standard deviation of the points about the fitted curve, to derive the required confidence limits. Graphs of some of the values are given for the benefit of those who prefer to use graphs.

The procedure for deriving the confidence limits is similar to that of Section 3.7.2. The deviations of the actual data from the fitted curve are obtained and their standard deviation is calculated, the divisor being $(n-3)$ as for the parabola. With n equal to the number of years in the period, and r the value in the fitted equation, Table Q is entered to find the required factor—or, alternatively, the factor is obtained from Graph F. The product of this factor and the standard deviation is then added to, and subtracted from, the predicted value to get the confidence limits.

Example

As an example, the confidence limits are derived for a value of demand for Commodity A predicted from the Gompertz curve.

The equation of the Gompertz curve for Commodity A, using the Gomes functions fitted, is:

$$\text{Log } Y = 1 \cdot 9355 - 0 \cdot 4778 \times (0 \cdot 8136)^t \text{ where } t = 1 \text{ for year 11.}$$

To derive the standard deviation of the points about the fitted line, we obtain values of log Y from this equation for $t = 1, 2, \ldots 11$. The actual and predicted values and their differences are given in the following table:

TABLE 9 – ESTIMATION OF
90% CONFIDENCE LIMITS FOR GOMPERTZ

Year	t	Actual Log Demand	Calculated Log Y	Calculated Log − Actual Log
11	1	1·5366	1·5468	0·0102
12	2	1·6284	1·6192	−0·0092
13	3	1·7110	1·6782	−0·0328
14	4	1·7076	1·7262	0·0186
15	5	1·7243	1·7652	0·0409
16	6	1·8048	1·7969	−0·0079
17	7	1·8357	1·8228	−0·0129
18	8	1·8543	1·8438	−0·0105
19	9	1·8519	1·8609	0·0090
20	10	1·9036	1·8748	−0·0288
21	11	1·8627	1·8861	0·0234
22	12	–	1·8954	–

$$S^2 = 0\cdot00508036$$

$$S^2/(n-3) = 0\cdot000635045$$

$$S/\sqrt{n-3} = 0\cdot0252.$$

The value of log Y for year 22 is obtained by substituting $t = 12$ in the equation, and is given in the last line of the above table.

We enter Table Q (or Graph F) for $n = 11$ and interpolate for $r = 0\cdot8136$ to derive the required factor; which is 1·425. Hence the logarithms of the confidence limits are 1·8954$\pm$0·0359. The antilogarithms are obtained to give the predicted value 78·6, and the 90 per cent. confidence limits 72·4, 85·4.

3.7.5. Confidence Limits for Individual Values

Although the confidence limits usually required are those described in the three previous sections, it was pointed out in Section 2.7.5 that there are occasions when interest lies in predicting individual values. The confidence limits required are then obtained by combining those for the uncertainty of the curve with those estimated from the scatter of the data, and these are combined by adding their squares and taking the square root. The first of them is obtained from Table F, G or Q. For the second, the relevant value of " Student's t " is used, and this is derived from Table F or G. For the straight line or the simple exponential the value of " Student's t " is obtained from the final column of Table F; for the parabola, logarithmic parabola or any of the modified exponential family " Student's t " is obtained from the final column of Table G. The number of demands used in fitting the curve gives the value of n. The squares of the two factors are added, the square root is taken and this result is multiplied by the standard deviation calculated as already described, and added to, and subtracted from, the predicted demand to give the confidence limits.

Examples

i) Parabola

Section 3.7.2 gives an example of calculating the usual confidence limits for the parabola. The required figures for the present computations are:

Value estimated for year 22 $= 76\cdot7$

Root mean square residual, i.e. $S/\sqrt{(n-3)} = 3\cdot41$

Factor G for $n = 12$, year $n+1$ $= 1\cdot895$

" Student's t " for $n = 12$ (from Table G) $= 1\cdot833$

Factor required for new confidence limits $= \sqrt{(1\cdot895^2 + 1\cdot833^2)} = 2\cdot64$

Hence confidence limits are: $76\cdot7\pm2\cdot64\times3\cdot41$, i.e. 67·7 and 85·7.

Note: The procedure is similar for the logarithmic parabola, except that logarithms are used. It must be remembered that all the calculations are carried out using logarithms; taking antilogarithms is the final step.

ii) Gompertz

Section 3.7.4 gives an example of the calculation of the usual confidence limits for the Gompertz. The estimation of the limits is as follows. Figures relating to demand, residual and the derived confidence limits are in logarithms.

Value estimated for year 22	$= 1 \cdot 8954$
Root mean square residual, i.e. $S/\sqrt{(n-3)}$	$= 0 \cdot 0252$
Factor Q for $n = 11$, $r = 0 \cdot 8136$	$= 1 \cdot 425$
" Student's t " for $n = 11$ (from Table G)	$= 1 \cdot 860$
Factor required for new confidence limits	$= \sqrt{(1 \cdot 425^2 + 1 \cdot 86^2)} = 2 \cdot 34$
Hence: Logarithms of confidence limits	$= 1 \cdot 8954 \pm 2 \cdot 34 \times 0 \cdot 0252$,
	i.e. $1 \cdot 8364$ and $1 \cdot 9544$

and the confidence limits are 68·6 and 90·0.

APPENDIX I

ALTERNATIVE METHODS FOR ESTIMATING THE SLOPES

The method suggested for computing the slope gives the most efficient estimate of the slope in that it provides an estimate with the least variance. Any unbiased estimate of the slope can be used instead. The simplest is the difference between the demand for two years (h) and $(h+2k)$ divided by $2k$ which gives the slope for year $(h+k)$. For a five-year period the efficiency of such an estimator is 80 per cent. and for a nine-year period 64 per cent. Another method which has been suggested is to divide the period into three sub-periods of which the first and last are equal in length. The difference between the averages for the first and third periods is proportional to the slope at the mid-point of the entire period. This estimate is most efficient when the three periods are equal and in such cases the efficiency is 90 per cent. This method provides an attractive alternative in some respects to the method proposed in the text, particularly as the loss of efficiency is very slight.

APPENDIX 2

GOMES FUNCTIONS FOR
THE FITTING OF MODIFIED EXPONENTIALS

Let $y_1, y_2, ..., y_n$ be the demand data.

Then the least squares or best fitting form of the modified exponential:

$$Y = a - br^t$$

is obtained by equating to zero the partial derivatives with respect to a, b and r of:

$$Z = \sum_1^n (y_t - a + br^t)^2$$

where $\sum_1^n$ stands for the sum of all such expressions from $t = 1$ to $t = n$.

a, b and r are given by the three equations:

$$\Sigma y_t - na + b\Sigma r^t = 0 \qquad \qquad ...(1)$$

$$\Sigma y_t r^t - a\Sigma r^t + b\Sigma r^{2t} = 0 \qquad \qquad ...(2)$$

$$\Sigma t y_t r^{t-1} - a\Sigma t r^{t-1} + b\Sigma t r^{2t-1} = 0 \qquad \qquad ...(3)$$

If a and b are eliminated from the above three equations an equation containing only r is obtained which can be written either in the determinantal form:

$$\begin{vmatrix} \Sigma y_t & n & \Sigma r^t \\ \Sigma y_t r^t & \Sigma r^t & \Sigma r^{2t} \\ \Sigma t y_t r^{t-1} & \Sigma t r^{t-1} & \Sigma t r^{2t-1} \end{vmatrix} = 0$$

or in the form

$$\Sigma y_t J_{n,t} = y_1 J_{n,1} + y_2 J_{n,2} + y_3 J_{n,3} + ... + y_n J_{n,n} = 0$$

where the J's are functions of r and are known as Gomes J functions.*

* When Gomes functions are not available, values of determinants may be plotted against values of r on either side of the approximate value obtained by the three-point method.

APPENDIX 3

THE SLOPE CHARACTERISTIC

When the commonly used mathematical trend curves are fitted to a set of data, it is usually found that the closeness of the fit is approximately the same for all the curves, i.e. there is little to choose between the curves as representation of the actual data. When the curves are extrapolated, however, they diverge, and even a small extrapolation may lead to unacceptably large divergences. It is natural, therefore, to look for some other means of comparing the curves for suitability for forecasting.

Since it may be assumed that differences between the curves may be neglected *over the range of the data*, projections of the curves into the future will depend on the rates of change of the various curves. For any curve $y = f(t)$, the rate of change, at any point of the curve, is given by the value of the derivative $dy/dt = f'(t)$ at that point. For the curves considered the principal differences between predictions will arise from differences between the derivatives. To test the suitability of the curves for prediction, therefore, we require to compare the curve representing the rate of change of demand with the derivatives. The curve most easily recognised is the straight line. We, therefore, find for each curve the transformation of the derivative which will yield a straight line with "t" as the independent variable. Each such transformation is applied to the estimated rates of change of the data at each year of the period and the results are plotted against time. It is then decided by inspection whether for any transformation of the rate of change, the plotted values appear to approximate to a straight line. Where a straight line is a reasonable fit, the corresponding curve may be expected to be a satisfactory predictor. It is convenient to use the word "slope" to mean the rate of change, and, since the transformations obtained characterise the curves, they are called "slope characteristics".

The various slope characteristics with their derivations are given below:

i) The Polynomials

The parabola is given by $y = a+bt+ct^2$ which includes the straight line as a special case when $c = 0$.

$$y = a+bt+ct^2$$

$$dy/dt = b+2ct.$$

This is a straight line and hence for the parabola the slope characteristic is the estimated slope.

Since for the straight line $c = 0$, the slope characteristic is also the estimated slope, with the additional restriction that the line obtained for the plotted estimates must be horizontal.

ii) The Exponentials

The logarithmic parabola is given by $\log y = a+bt+ct^2$, the simple exponential being the special case where $c = 0$.

$$\log y = a+bt+ct^2$$

$$(1/y)(dy/dt) = b+2ct.$$

The function which yields a straight line is, therefore, the ratio of the slope to the expected value, and this is the slope characteristic.

For the simple exponential, with $c = 0$, there is the additional restriction that the plotted ratios must yield a horizontal line.

iii) The Modified Exponentials

a) The simple modified exponential is $y = a - br^t$.

$$y = a - br^t$$

$$dy/dt = -b.\log r . r^t$$

Therefore $\log (dy/dt) = \log (-b.\log r) + t \log r.$

The slope characteristic of the simple modified exponential is the logarithm of the estimated slope. Further, since $r < 1$, the slope of the resulting straight line must be negative.

b) The Gompertz curve is:

$$\log y = a - br^t$$

$$(1/y)(dy/dt) = -b.\log r . r^t$$

Therefore $\log \{(1/y)(dy/dt)\} = \log (-b.\log r) + t \log r.$

The slope characteristic of the Gompertz curve is, therefore, the logarithm of the ratio of the slope to the expected values. Further, since for trend curves the value of r must be less than unity, the slope of the line obtained must be negative for a Gompertz curve to be acceptable.

c) The logistic curve is:

$$1/y = a + br^t$$

Therefore $(-1/y^2)(dy/dt) = b.\log r . r^t$ i.e. $(1/y^2)(dy/dt) = -b.\log r . r^t$

Therefore $\log \{(1/y^2)(dy/dt)\} = \log (-b.\log r) + t \log r.$

The slope characteristic of the logistic curve is, therefore, the logarithm of the ratio of the slope to the square of the expected value. Since r must be less than unity the term $-b.\log r$ is positive so that its logarithm is real. Further, the slope of the line obtained must be negative for a satisfactory logistic curve to be obtained.

Note: The principal advantage of using a modified exponential as a trend curve is that a curve is obtained which asymptotically approaches a maximum value. This is only true where the value of r is less than unity, and this restriction is therefore always accepted.

For this technique to be used it is necessary to estimate the slope at each year of the series, and, for some of the curves, to obtain estimates of the expected values. Because of the fluctuations from year to year, the actual demands and simple differences are not considered satisfactory for the purpose. Some smoothing is necessary and for the estimated demands this is done by using moving averages for the expected values. To obtain an estimate of the slope for a given year, a short period (usually 5, 7 or 9 years) is chosen with the given year at the middle. The average slope over this period is then calculated and this is used as the slope for the given year. The expected values and slopes so obtained are then used with the formulae of the previous section to plot the slope characteristics for the various curves.

To examine the technique adequately will require not only the application of the technique to data for a large number of commodities, but also a comprehensive study of how satisfactory the various curves are as predictors. In addition comparisons will have to be made between the curve chosen in any example and the other curves which might have been used. The technique can be said to be completely successful only if the curve indicated by the technique can be shown on the average to be superior to the others. Such an investigation will take a considerable time.

Up to the present it has been possible to test the technique only on its ability to indicate if one curve is likely to be superior to the others.

APPENDIX 4

THE GENERAL MODIFIED EXPONENTIAL

i) Fitting the General Modified Exponential

All the three modified exponentials are particular or limiting cases of the general modified exponential:

$$Y = (a + br^t)^\phi$$

which again will normally have an asymptotic approach to a ceiling market a^ϕ. From this expression the following can be derived:

$$\log \frac{dY}{dt} - \frac{(\phi - 1)}{\phi} \log Y = \log (\phi b \log r) + t \log r. \qquad \qquad \ldots(1)$$

This is the slope characteristic. If the left-hand side is plotted against t, it should show a linear trend if the modified exponential fits the demand data.

An examination of Commodity A will show that in passing from the simple modified exponential, $\phi = 1$, to the logistic $\phi = -1$, the linearity of the slope characteristic improves. Providing that the point of discontinuity around year 10 was supported by some major change in market conditions, fitting a trend which was only consistent for the latter part of the demand data would be justified, but otherwise it would at best be a compromise.

For illustrating the fitting of trend curves, it has been implicitly assumed in the text that there was some justification for a change in market conditions for Commodity A at year 10. If this were not so, then the trend curves could well be little more than interpolation formulae, useful for this purpose but providing diminished intuitive reassurance concerning the validity of their extrapolation. In these circumstances it would be preferable to find a curve which provided a reasonable fit to the entire period. With an S-shaped curve it is possible that an alternative form of the modified exponential might provide a better basis. This would involve the estimation of ϕ.

It is a necessary though not sufficient condition for a modified exponential to fit the data that:

$$\log \frac{dY}{dt} - \frac{\phi - 1}{\phi} \log Y$$

plotted against time should show no sign of non-linearity. A modified exponential to satisfy the condition can be obtained as follows:

Defining
$$x = \log \frac{dY}{dt} - \frac{1}{n} \Sigma \log \frac{dY}{dt}$$

$$y = \log Y - \frac{1}{n} \Sigma \log Y$$

$$T = t - \frac{n+1}{2} \quad t = 1, 2, \ldots n$$

then substituting these variables in expression (1) gives the sum of squares:

$$\Sigma \left\{ x - \frac{\phi-1}{\phi}\, y - kT \right\}^2$$

which, when minimised, leads to:

$$\frac{\phi-1}{\phi} = \frac{(\Sigma\, xy)(\Sigma\, T^2)-(\Sigma\, Ty)(\Sigma\, Tx)}{(\Sigma\, y^2)(\Sigma\, T^2)-(\Sigma\, Ty)^2}.$$

Estimates of $\dfrac{dY}{dt}$ and Y are supplied by the slope and the moving average, and by using these estimates a value of ϕ can be derived.

If this formula is applied to Commodity A, the value of $\phi = -0\cdot4$ approximately is obtained. The slope characteristic for this value of ϕ is illustrated in Figure 10 and shows reasonable linearity through the range $t = 1$ to $t = 21$.

Choosing the criterion for fitting the actual trend based on this form of the general modified exponential raises a difficulty which is already present in fitting the logistic, but is even more serious in this type of modified exponential curve, with $\phi = -0\cdot4$ instead of the logistic, $\phi = -1$. The three curves obtained by the conventional methods proposed in the text make different assumptions about the variability of the demand data, and further, whilst the assumptions in the case of the Gompertz and simple modified exponential, though different, are reasonable, the assumption made for the logistic is unreasonable in most conceivable cases. For the Gompertz the inference is that the coefficient of variation of the demand data is constant, whilst the simple modified exponential implies that the variance of the demand is constant. When fitting the logistic the assumption is that the coefficient of variation is inversely proportional to the absolute magnitude of the demand. The practical effect of this is to give undue weight to the early demand data. This is a serious enough weakness in the above method of fitting the logistic, but in a modified exponential with $\phi = -0\cdot4$, very little weight indeed is given to later demand data by this method, so that they have little effect on the estimation of the parameters. It is highly desirable, if not imperative, to use a weighted sum of squares for fitting the modified exponentials other than the Gompertz and the simple modified exponential. The mathematical theory is given in Appendix 5, and computer programmes have been, and can be derived, to apply this theory with arbitrary weights or such as are consistent with the assumption that the coefficient of variation is constant, no matter what form of the modified exponential is used. In designing a computer programme to fit the general modified exponential, it is only necessary to programme for the fitting of the simple modified exponential with constant coefficient of variation, coupled with the ability to transform the input data D to $D^{1/\phi}$, either within the programme or before feeding in the data. For all values of ϕ, the fitting will assume a constant coefficient of variation for D.

Such a programme has been used to find the general modified exponential with $\phi = -0\cdot4$ to the demand data for Commodity A and the trend values are shown on p. 50.

ii) General Comments on Fitting Modified Exponentials

It will be noted that the market for Commodity A is apparently reaching its ceiling value. In such cases it would be appropriate to acknowledge this fact and ascertain whether the ceiling market for the product was likely to be fixed or would show a gradual expansion relative to the growth in the general national economy or some more precise part of the economy, as for instance a particular group of industries. If a growth in the ceiling market was considered reasonable in the light of market information, then the procedure referred to

FIGURE IO-GENERAL MODIFIED EXPONENTIAL $Y= (a+br^t)\phi$

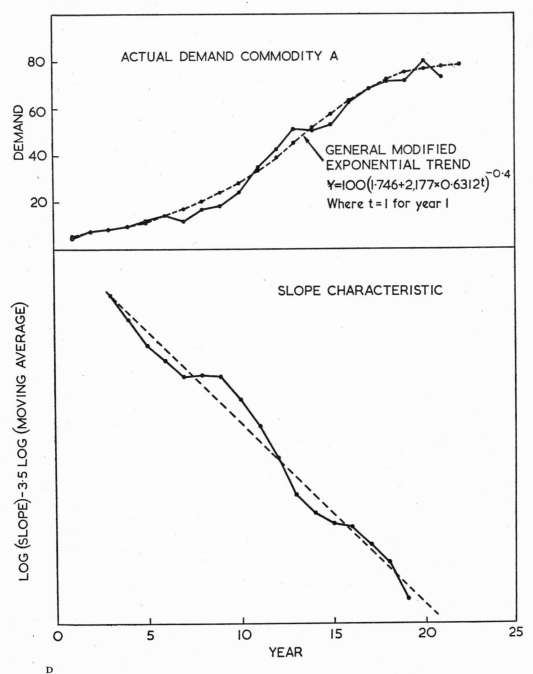

ACTUAL DEMAND COMMODITY A

GENERAL MODIFIED
EXPONENTIAL TREND
$Y=100(1\cdot746+2,177\times0\cdot6312^t)^{-0\cdot4}$
Where $t=1$ for year 1

SLOPE CHARACTERISTIC

DEMAND

LOG (SLOPE)-3·5 LOG (MOVING AVERAGE)

YEAR

D

in Section 3.6 should be applied to the more recent demand data. It is unlikely that a suitable index of the ceiling market would be available for an extensive period.

Commodity A is an example of a product near its saturation market. In the early stages of the growth of such a demand, it is sometimes possible to determine with fair accuracy the eventual ceiling demand. In these circumstances exponential trends can be used to estimate the growth towards such a ceiling market based on the existing information on the growth of

Comparison of Commodity A demand data and the
general modified exponential trend

Year	Demand	General Modified Exponential
1	5·7	5·6
2	6·9	6·7
3	8·5	8·0
4	9·6	9·7
5	11·6	11·6
6	14·1	13·9
7	12·4	16·7
8	16·0	19·9
9	18·2	23·8
10	23·8	28·3
11	34·4	33·4
12	42·5	39·2
13	51·4	45·4
14	51·0	52·0
15	53·0	57·9
16	63·8	63·4
17	68·5	68·1
18	71·5	72·5
19	71·1	75·3
20	80·1	76·3
21	72·9	77·6
Forecast		
26		79·9
28		79·9
Ceiling demand		80·0

The trend values are also shown in Figure 10.

the demand and the estimated ceiling demand. Having determined the form of the general exponential, the exponential parameters " b " and " r " are then estimated for the postulated ceiling demand. If the form of the general exponential is:

$$Y = (a+br^t)^\phi$$

and A is the postulated ceiling market,

then $Y^{1/\phi} = a+br^t$ and $a = A^{1/\phi}$.

Hence $\log (Y^{1/\phi} - A^{1/\phi}) = \log b + t \log r$.

The values of $\log b$ and $\log r$ can be obtained by using the factors in Table D, applied to $\log (y^{1/\phi} - A^{1/\phi})$ where y is the actual demand data.

This procedure would be advisable when the market is obviously well below its maximum, particularly when the point of inflexion, i.e. the point where the slope ceases to increase, has not been reached.

APPENDIX 5

MATHEMATICAL BASIS
FOR FITTING MODIFIED EXPONENTIALS

i) Weighting

The curve to be fitted is:

$$y = a + bR^t = a + b \exp(\rho t) \qquad \text{...(1)}$$

where a, b and R are constants with $1 > R > 0$, $\rho = \ln R$, t is time measured from some arbitrary zero and, if Y is the rate of demand at time t,

$$\left.\begin{array}{ll}
y = \log_{10} Y & \text{for the Gompertz curve} \\
y = Y & \text{for the ordinary modified exponential curve} \\
y = 1/Y & \text{for the logistic curve} \\
y = Y^1/\Phi & \text{for general modified exponential curve where } \Phi \text{ is an arbitrary} \\
& \text{constant, whose value will be assumed to be known, such that } |\Phi| \\
& \text{is appreciably greater than zero.}
\end{array}\right\} \quad \text{...(2)}$$

A number of observations Y_j of the value of Y at times t_j are available, and from (2) these may be converted into observations of y_j the value of y at times t_j. It will be assumed that the y_j are independently distributed round the expected value $a + b \exp(\rho_j^t)$, but that variance of this distribution is not the same for all the observations. Let this variance be K/w_j where K is a constant and w_j is a weighting factor inversely proportional to the expected variance of y_j. If we define a new variable z such that

$$z_j = y_j \sqrt{w_j} \qquad \text{...(3)}$$

the observed values of z_j will be independently distributed round the expected value

$$\{a + b \exp(\rho t_j)\}\sqrt{w_j}$$

with a variance that is the same for all the observations. Optimum (least squares) estimates of a, b and ρ (or R) may therefore be obtained by minimising the sum of the squares of the deviations of z_j, i.e. by minimising

$$\Delta = \sum_j w_j \{y_j - a - b \exp(\rho t_j)\}^2. \qquad \text{...(4)}$$

The magnitude of the weighting factors w_j will depend both on the type of curve being fitted and on the assumptions made with regard to the expected variance of the individual Y_j. To a first approximation

$$w_j = K/V(y_j) = K/\{(dy/dY)^2 V(Y_j)\}$$

where K is an arbitrary constant of any convenient magnitude.

$$\left.\begin{array}{l}
= K(2 \cdot 302585 Y_j)^2/V(Y_j) \text{ Gompertz} \\
= K/V(Y_j) \text{ modified exponential} \\
= K Y_j^4/V(Y_j) \text{ logistic} \\
= K_\Phi^2/\{Y_j^{2(1-\Phi)/\Phi} V(Y_j)\} \text{ general modified exponential.}
\end{array}\right\} \quad \text{...(5)}$$

51

In the above it is assumed that the variance of Y_j about its expected value is small compared with the total variance. This will normally be the case with economic data in which the changes in Y_j are usually large. If the assumption is untrue the weighted fit will be somewhat biased.

There are many possible assumptions that might be made about the variance $V(Y_j)$; four of these will be considered in the following sections.

(a) *Unweighted Fit.* This is equivalent to $w_j = 1$; $j = 1(1)n$. For the Gompertz this implies $V(Y_j)/Y_j^2 = $ constant, i.e. that the coefficient of variation of Y_j is constant.

For the modified exponential this implies that $V(Y_j) = $ constant, i.e. that the standard deviation of Y_j is constant.

For the logistic this implies that $V(Y_j)/Y_j^4 = $ constant, i.e. that the coefficient of variation of Y_j is inversely proportional to the absolute magnitude of Y_j. Such an assumption would be most difficult to justify for any ordinary set of data, it is, however, the type of fit frequently employed for this curve.

For general modified exponential curve this implies that the coefficient of variation of Y_j is inversely proportional to $Y_j^{1/\Phi}$. As before this is, in general, unlikely to be true.

(b) *Fit Subject to Arbitrary Weights.* For this purpose each value of Y_j is associated with a measure α_j of its per cent. accuracy, so that $V(Y_j) = 10^{-4}k^2 Y_j^2 \alpha_j^2$ where k is an arbitrary constant depending on the standard used in assessing α_j. If α_j is an estimate of the per cent. coefficient of variation of Y_j than $k = 1$.

Taking the arbitrary constant $K = k^2$ this gives

$$\left.\begin{aligned}
w_j &= (230 \cdot 2585)^2/\alpha_j^2 \text{ for the Gompertz} \\
w_j &= 10^4/Y_j^2 \alpha_j^2 \text{ for the modified exponential} \\
w_j &= 10^4 Y_j^2/\alpha_j^2 \text{ for the logistic} \\
w_j &= 10^4 \Phi^2/Y_j^{2/\Phi} \alpha_j^2 \text{ for general modified exponential}
\end{aligned}\right\} \quad \ldots(6)$$

If the variable z is defined $x_j = y_j \sqrt{w_j}$ as in (3) the expected variance of z will be k^2 for all observations. The standard deviation of z about its expected value will therefore be a measure of the ratio of the true coefficient of variation to estimated coefficient.

A method of weighting which is often favoured is to give exponential weights to the demand, the most recent demand being given the highest weight. This can readily be done by making the α_j^2 into an exponentially increasing series, the α_j^2 for the most recent demand being the smallest.

(c) *Fit assuming Constant Coefficient of Variation for Y_j.* For a Gompertz curve this is the same as an unweighted fit and has not been separately programmed.

For the modified exponential and the logistic the required weights may be obtained from (6) by making all the values of α equal. For convenience the value $\alpha = 1$ has been chosen.

$$\left.\begin{aligned}
w_j &= 10^4/Y_j^2 \text{ for the modified exponential} \\
w_j &= 10^4 Y_j^2 \text{ for the logistic} \\
w_j &= 10^4 \Phi^2/Y^{2/\Phi} \text{ for general modified exponential}
\end{aligned}\right\} \quad \ldots(7)$$

The standard deviation of z about is expected value will then be a measure of the per cent. coefficient of variation of the Y_j.

(d) It has been pointed out by Dr O. L. Davies that it is almost always possible to find a power transformation of the demand data (Y_j^β) for which the variance of $V(Y_j^\beta)$ becomes reasonably constant. The expression to be minimised becomes

$$\Sigma[Y_j^\beta - \{a + b \exp (\rho t)\}^{\beta \Phi}]^2.$$

This is equivalent to setting α_j in (b) above equal to $100/\beta Y_j^\beta$. The corresponding values of w_j are given by:

$$w_j = 5 \cdot 3019 \, \beta^2 Y_j^{2\beta} \qquad \text{Gompertz}$$

$$w_j = \beta^2 Y_j^{2(\beta - 1)} \qquad \text{ordinary modified exponential}$$

$$w_j = \beta^2 Y_j^{2(\beta + 1)} \qquad \text{logistic}$$

$$w_j = \beta^2 \Phi^2 Y_j^{2(\beta - 1/\Phi)} \qquad \text{general modified exponential.}$$

If it is desired to fit the curves subject to any other assumption as to the nature of the variability of Y, this can readily be done by using arbitrary weights. For example, to fit a Gompertz or Logistic assuming a constant standard deviation for Y, i.e. a constant absolute, as opposed to percentage, accuracy for the observed demands, a set of values of α equal to $100/Y$ might be inserted.

ii) Finding Values of Constants

As shown in the previous section $z_j = y_j \sqrt{w_j}$ will vary round its expected value

$$\{a + b \exp (\rho t)\}\sqrt{w}$$

with constant variance. To find optimum values of a, b and ρ we must minimise:

$$\Delta = \Sigma[w_j \{y_j - a - b \exp (\rho t_j)\}^2].$$

The normal equations are therefore:

$$-2\Sigma[w_j \{y_j - a - b \exp (\rho t_j)\}] = 0$$

$$-2\Sigma[w_j \exp (\rho t_j)\{y_j - a - b \exp (\rho t_j)\}] = 0$$

$$-2b\Sigma[w_j t_j \exp (\rho t_j)\{y_j - a - b \exp (\rho t_j)\}] = 0$$

or

$$a\Sigma w_j + b\Sigma w_j \exp (\rho t_j) = \Sigma w_j y_j$$

$$a\Sigma\{w_j \exp (\rho t_j)\} + b\Sigma\{w_j \exp (2\rho t_j)\} = \Sigma\{w_j y_j \exp (\rho t_j)\}$$

$$ab\Sigma\{w_j t_j \exp (\rho t_j)\} + b^2\Sigma\{w_j t_j \exp (2\rho t_j)\} = b\Sigma\{w_j y_j t_j \exp (\rho t_j)\}. \qquad \ldots(8)$$

These normal equations are not readily soluble in the general case, though methods of solution are known when the t_j are an evenly spaced set of integers.

If the curves are to be of the required form, approaching a limiting value at large t, the value of R must be between 0 and 1 and usually between $0 \cdot 5$ and 1. For any given value of R (and therefore of $\rho = \ln R$), a and b, and hence Δ, may be found from

$$a\Sigma w_j + b\Sigma w_j \exp (\rho t_j) = \Sigma w_j y_j$$

$$a\Sigma\{w_j \exp (\rho t_j)\} + b\Sigma\{w_j \exp (2\rho t_j)\} = \Sigma\{w_j y_j \exp (\rho t_j)\} \qquad \ldots(9)$$

from which we obtain:

$$b = \frac{\Sigma w_j \Sigma\{w_j y_j \exp (\rho t_j)\} - \Sigma w_j y_j \Sigma\{w_j \exp (\rho t_j)\}}{\Sigma w_j \Sigma\{w_j \exp (2\rho t_j)\} - [\Sigma\{w_j \exp (\rho t_j)\}]^2} \qquad \ldots(10)$$

$$a = [\Sigma w_j y_j - b\Sigma\{w_j \exp (\rho t_j)\}]/\Sigma w_j \qquad \ldots(11)$$

$$\Delta = [\Sigma\{w_j y_j^2\} - \{\Sigma w_j y_j\}^2/\Sigma w_j] - b[\Sigma\{w_j y_j \exp (\rho t_j)\} - \Sigma w_j y_j \Sigma\{w_j \exp (\rho t_j)\}/\Sigma w_j]. \ \ldots(12)$$

The method of solution adopted is to evaluate Δ by (10), (11) and (12) for a series of values of R and to select the value of R giving the lowest value of Δ.

There are a number of methods of doing this that might be used in a computer programme. One relatively simple method that has been used in a programme and found to work satisfactorily is as follows.

Since normally $0.5 < R < 1.0$ the initial search is made with 9 values of R, $0.55(0.05)0.95$. The step length is then divided by 5 and the search repeated for a further set of 9 values centred round the selected value of R. This procedure is repeated till the step length is small enough to give the required accuracy in R. Normally 4 sets of 9 values of R are tested giving a step length of 0.0004 in the last set.

If the final R is the largest tried, one further set of values is tried and if R is still at its highest possible value " No Fit " is printed.

If the final R is the lowest tried the whole procedure is repeated starting from $R = 0.15$ $(0.05)0.55$, if after this the final R is still the lowest tried " No Fit " is printed.

This procedure for solving the normal equations, though somewhat slower than possible alternatives, was chosen as it is likely to be robust against possible oddities in the behaviour of the function.

The final minimum value of Δ gives the sum of the squares of z about its expected value, from which the variance and standard deviation of z may be found.

iii) Standard Errors and Confidence Limits

The treatment adopted in this section follows in general outline, though not in detail, the treatment used by W. L. Stevens, Biometrics 1951, **7**, 247, and by Dr J. T. Richardson of Billingham Division in a draft memorandum to Study Group 3 of the Statistical Methods Panel.

The equation $y_j = a + b \exp{(\rho t_j)}$ may be rewritten as

$$y_j = a + bm + b(\exp{(\rho t_j)} - m)$$
$$= k + bu_j \qquad \qquad \text{...(13)}$$

where
$$m = \Sigma(w_j \exp{(\rho t_j)})/\Sigma w_j \qquad \qquad \text{...(14)}$$
$$k = a + bm \qquad \qquad \text{...(15)}$$
$$u_j = \exp{(\rho t_j)} - m. \qquad \qquad \text{...(16)}$$

Let
$$v_j = \partial u_j/\partial \rho = t_j \exp{(\rho t_j)} - \Sigma(w_j t_j \exp{(\rho t_j)})/\Sigma w_j \qquad \qquad \text{...(17)}$$

then
$$\partial v_j/\partial \rho = \partial^2 u_j/(\partial \rho)^2 = t_j^2 \exp{(\rho t_j)} - \Sigma(w_j t_j^2 \exp{(\rho t_j)})/\Sigma w_j \qquad \qquad \text{...(18)}$$
$$\Sigma w_j u_j = \Sigma w_j v_j = \Sigma w_j(\partial v_j/\partial \rho) = 0. \qquad \qquad \text{...(19)}$$

As in the first section we may define a new variable

$$z_j = y_j\sqrt{w_j}$$

and minimise
$$\Delta = \Sigma(z_j - \sqrt{w_j}(k + bu_j))^2$$
$$= \Sigma(w_j(y_j - k - bu_j)^2)$$

with respect to the constants k, b and ρ.

The normal equations are:

$$-2\Sigma(w_j(y_j-k-bu_j)) = 0 \qquad \text{...(20)}$$
$$-2\Sigma(w_ju_j(y_j-k-bu_j)) = 0 \qquad \text{...(21)}$$
$$-2b\Sigma(w_jv_j(y_j-k-bu_j)) = 0 \qquad \text{...(22)}$$

from (19) $\Sigma w_ju_j = \Sigma w_jv_j = 0$.

The normal equations therefore reduce to

$$k\Sigma w_j-\Sigma w_jy_j = 0 \qquad \text{...(23)}$$
$$b\Sigma w_ju_j^2-\Sigma w_ju_jy_j = 0 \qquad \text{...(24)}$$
$$b^2\Sigma w_ju_jv_j-b\Sigma w_jv_jy_j = 0. \qquad \text{...(25)}$$

The information matrix:

$$
\begin{array}{lll}
\partial^2\Delta/(\partial k)^2 & \partial^2\Delta/(\partial k\partial b) & \partial^2\Delta/(\partial k\partial\rho) \\
\partial^2\Delta/(\partial b\partial k) & \partial^2\Delta/(\partial b)^2 & \partial^2\Delta/(\partial b\partial\rho) \\
\partial^2\Delta/(\partial\rho\partial k) & \partial^2\Delta/(\partial\rho\partial b) & \partial^2\Delta/(\partial\rho)^2
\end{array}
\qquad \text{...(26)}
$$

may be obtained by differentiating (23), (24) and (25) with respect to k, b and ρ.

It is:

$$
\begin{array}{lll}
\Sigma w_j & 0 & 0 \\
0 & \Sigma w_ju_j^2 & [2b\Sigma w_ju_jv_j-\Sigma w_jv_jy_j] \\
0 & [2b\Sigma w_ju_jv_j-\Sigma w_jv_jy_j] & [b^2\Sigma w_jv_j^2+b^2\Sigma w_ju_j(\partial v_j/\partial\rho)-b\Sigma w_jy_j(\partial v_j/\partial\rho)].
\end{array}
\qquad \text{...(27)}
$$

Substituting for y_j its expected value $(k+bu_j)$ and remembering (19) that

$$\Sigma w_ju_j = \Sigma w_jv_j = \Sigma w_j(\partial v/\partial\rho) = 0$$

this becomes:

$$
\begin{array}{lll}
\Sigma w_j & 0 & 0 \\
0 & \Sigma w_ju_j^2 & b\Sigma w_ju_jv_j \\
0 & b\Sigma w_ju_jv_j & b^2\Sigma w_jv_j^2
\end{array}
\qquad \text{...(28)}
$$

If $D = b^2[\Sigma w_ju_j^2\Sigma w_jv_j-(\Sigma w_ju_jv_j)^2]$, the inverse of the above matrix is:

$$
\begin{array}{lll}
1/\Sigma w_j & 0 & 0 \\
0 & (b^2\Sigma w_jv_j^2)/D & -(b\Sigma w_ju_jv_j)/D \\
0 & -(b\Sigma w_ju_jv_j)/D & (\Sigma w_ju_j^2)/D
\end{array}
\qquad \text{...(29)}
$$

If therefore σ^2 is the variance of z_j about its expected value $\sqrt{w_j}(k+bu_j)$, the variances of the estimates of constants k, b and ρ are given by:

$$V(k) = \sigma^2/\Sigma w_j \qquad \text{...(30)}$$
$$V(b) = (b^2\sigma^2/D)(\Sigma w_jv_j^2) \qquad \text{...(31)}$$
$$V(\rho) = (\sigma^2/D)(\Sigma w_ju_j^2) \qquad \text{...(32)}$$
$$\text{Cov}(b, \rho) = -(b\sigma^2/D)(\Sigma w_ju_jv_j) \qquad \text{...(33)}$$
$$\text{Cov}(k, b) = \text{Cov}(k_1\rho) = 0 \qquad \text{...(34)}$$

or in terms of the original variable " t ",

$$V(k) = \sigma^2/\Sigma w_j$$

$$V(b) = (b^2\sigma^2/D)[\Sigma(w_j t_j^2 \exp(2\rho t_j)) - (\Sigma w_j t_j \exp(\rho t_j))^2/\Sigma w_j]$$

$$V(\rho) = (\sigma^2/D)[\Sigma(w_j \exp(2\rho t_j)) - (\Sigma w_j \exp(\rho t_j))^2/\Sigma w_j]$$

$$\text{Cov}(b, \rho) = (-b\sigma^2/D)[\Sigma(w_j t_j \exp(2\rho t_j)) - (\Sigma w_j \exp(\rho t_j))(\Sigma w_j t_j \exp(\rho t_j))/\Sigma w_j$$

$$(D/b^2) = [\Sigma w_j \exp(2\rho t_j) - (\Sigma w_j \exp(\rho t_j))^2/\Sigma w_j][\Sigma w_j t_j^2 \exp(2\rho t_j) - (\Sigma w_j t_j \exp(\rho t_j))/$$

$$(\Sigma w_j)] - [\Sigma w_j t_j \exp(2\rho t_j) - (\Sigma w_j \exp(\rho t_j))(\Sigma w_j t_j \exp(\rho t_j))/\Sigma w]^2.$$

Since $R = \exp(\rho)$ the variance of the original constant R is given by:

$$V(R) = R^2 V(\rho). \qquad \qquad \text{...(35)}$$

Since from (14) and (15)

$$a = k - b(\Sigma w_j \exp(\rho t_j))/\Sigma w$$

$$\partial a/\partial k = 1$$

$$\partial a/\partial b = -(\Sigma w_j \exp(\rho t_j))/\Sigma w_j$$

$$\partial a/\partial \rho = -b(\Sigma w_j t_j \exp(\rho t_j))/\Sigma w_j$$

the variance of the original constant a is given by:

$$V(a) = V(k) + [(\Sigma w_j \exp(\rho t_j))/\Sigma w_j]^2(V(b)) + [b(\Sigma w_j t_j \exp(\rho t_j))/\Sigma w]^2(V(\rho))$$

$$+ 2[(\Sigma w_j \exp(\rho t_j))/\Sigma w_j][(\Sigma w_j t_j \exp(\rho t_j))/\Sigma w_j](\text{Cov}(b, \rho)) \qquad \text{...(36)}$$

If y_f is the forecasted value of the demand at time T

$$y_f = k + bu_f = k + b(\exp(\rho T) - m) \qquad \qquad \text{...(37)}$$

where $m = (\Sigma w_j \exp(\rho t_j))/\Sigma w_j$

$$\partial y_f/\partial k = 1$$

$$\partial y_f/\partial b = \exp(\rho T) - m = u_f \qquad \qquad \text{...(38)}$$

$$\partial y_f/\partial \rho = bT \exp(\rho T) - (\Sigma w_j t_j \exp(\rho t))/\Sigma w_j = v_f. \qquad \text{...(39)}$$

The variance of this forecasted value is therefore:

$$V(y_f) = V(k) + u_f^2(V(b)) + v_f^2(V(\rho)) + 2u_f v_f(\text{Cov}(b, \rho))$$

where u_f and v_f are defined by (38) and (39) and $V(k)$, $V(b)$, $V(\rho)$ and $\text{Cov}(b, \rho)$ are given by (30) to (33).

iv) Case when constant "a" is given

If "a" is known it would in principle be possible to transform $y = a + b \exp(\rho t)$ into the form $\ln(y-a) = \ln b + \rho t$ and to fit this as a linear regression using a set of weights w_j such that the variance of $z = \sqrt{w} \ln(y_j - a)$ is constant. If this were the only problem being programmed this is the method which would be used. In the present case, however, the full calculation for $z = y\sqrt{w}$ is already in the programme, and it is easier to make minor adjustments in this than to programme a different, though quicker, method of calculation; this section is, in any case, likely to be less used than the main calculation, for fitting ρ, b and a. The calculation is as follows:

$$\text{minimise } \Delta = \Sigma w_j\{y_j - a - b \exp(\rho t_j)\}^2 \qquad \text{...(40)}$$

which gives the normal equations

$$a\Sigma w_j \exp(\rho t_j) + b\Sigma w_j \exp(2\rho t_j) - \Sigma w_j y_j \exp(\rho t_j) = 0$$

$$ab\Sigma w_j t_j \exp(\rho t_j) + b^2\Sigma w_j t_j \exp(2\rho t_j) - b\Sigma w_j y_j t_j \exp(\rho t) = 0 \qquad \text{...(41)}$$

for a and ρ given

$$b = [\Sigma w_j y_j \exp(\rho t_j) - a\Sigma w_j \exp(\rho t_j)]/\{\Sigma w_j \exp(2\rho t_j)\} \qquad \text{...(42)}$$

$$\Delta = \Sigma w_j y_j^2 - 2a\Sigma w_j y_j + a^2\Sigma w_j - b\{\Sigma w_j y_j \exp(\rho t_j) - a\Sigma w_j \exp(\rho t_j)\} \qquad \text{...(43)}$$

optimum values of b and ρ are found by trial as in the previous case. The information matrix is

$$
\begin{matrix}
\Sigma w_j \exp(2\rho t_j) & b\Sigma w_j t_j \exp(2\rho t_j) \\
b\Sigma w_j t_j \exp(2\rho t_j) & b^2\Sigma w_j t_j^2 \exp(2\rho t_j)
\end{matrix}
\qquad \text{...(44)}
$$

whence if

$$D = b^2[\{\Sigma w_j \exp(2\rho t_j)\}\{\Sigma w_j t_j^2 \exp(2\rho t_j)\} - \{\Sigma w_j t_j \exp(2\rho t_j)\}^2] \qquad \text{...(45)}$$

$$V(b) = (b^2\sigma^2/D)\{\Sigma w_j t_j^2 \exp(2\rho t_j)\} \qquad \text{...(46)}$$

$$V(\rho) = (\sigma^2/D)\{\Sigma w_j \exp(2\rho t_j)\} \qquad \text{...(47)}$$

$$\text{Cov}(b, \rho) = (-b\sigma^2/D)\{\Sigma w_j t_j \exp(2\rho t_j)\}. \qquad \text{...(48)}$$

APPENDIX 6

COMPUTER PROGRAMMES AVAILABLE FROM IMPERIAL CHEMICAL INDUSTRIES LIMITED

ICI/M/582A MOVING AVERAGE AND SLOPE CHARACTERISTICS

Using given data for consecutive periods of equal length, the programme constructs and prints the moving average (over a specified odd number of periods) and five different slope characteristics. These are: slope; slope/moving average; log slope; log (slope/moving average); log (slope/moving average^2).

ICI/M/582B TREND EXTRAPOLATION

The programme fits up to seven curves to data given for consecutive periods of equal length. All or some of the following may be fitted: straight line, parabola, simple exponential, log parabola, modified exponential, logistic and Gompertz. A total of up to 153 intervals may be used, and the programme prints the parameters of each curve, the actual demand, the forecast values and the 90 per cent. confidence limits.

Programme ICI/M/582A will provide preliminary information on forecasting applications. If it is necessary to weight the data, ICI/M/582B gives a more comprehensive trend curve analysis. Weighting the data can be done for some of the possible trend curves by using one of the other programmes.

ICI/M/655 WEIFITMODEX

The programme is designed to fit the three curves which are derived from the modified exponential function $u = a + br^t$:

    a) Simple Modified Exponential   where u = demand Y
    b) Gompertz   where u = log (demand Y)
    c) Logistic   where u = 1/(demand Y)

where a, b and r are constants and " t " is a series of integers representing time, i.e. $t = 1, 2...$ for periods 1, 2.... The method used is an iterative one, minimising the sum of the squared deviations of u, unweighted or weighted by powers of Y (according to a given table).

ICI/M/361 GOMPLOT

The programme is used to obtain a Gompertz curve, fitting a given set of regularly spaced data, and to extrapolate the curve to assist in the estimation of future markets.

ICI/M/533B GOM-WEIGHTED

The programme is designed to extend the method of fitting curves derived from the modified exponential function $Y = a + br^t$ to cases where the data are given at arbitrary times, either with or without an estimate of each per cent. accuracy. The programme will also deal with the case in which the limiting value of the demand at distant times is given.

Copies of any of these programmes may be obtained on application free of charge (see Foreword).

TABLES AND GRAPHS

TABLE A – COMMODITY A: SLOPE AND TREND ANALYSIS

	CALCULATION OF 5 YEAR MOVING AVERAGE						CALCULATION OF SLOPE CHARACTERISTICS					
Year	Demand	Cumulative Demand		5 × Moving Average	M.A. Slope Year		Straight Line or Parabola	Simple Modified Exponential	Simple Exponential or Log Parabola	Gompertz		Logistic
1	2	3	4	5	6	7	8	9	10	11	12	13
1	5.7	5.7										
2	6.9	12.6										
3	8.5	21.1										
4	9.6	30.7										
5	11.6	42.3		42.3	3		14.5	0.161	0.343	1.535	0.811	1.909
6	14.1	56.4	5.7	50.7	4	5.7	17.5	0.243	0.345	1.538	0.680	1.833
7	12.4	68.8	12.6	56.2	5	6.9	12.3	0.090	0.219	1.340	0.390	1.591
8	16.0	84.8	21.1	63.7	6	8.5	13.6	0.134	0.214	1.330	0.336	1.526
9	18.2	103.0	30.7	72.3	7	9.6	15.1	0.179	0.209	1.320	0.289	1.461
10	23.8	126.8	42.3	84.5	8	11.6	25.2	0.401	0.298	1.474	0.353	1.548
11	34.4	161.2	56.4	104.8	9	14.1	51.8	0.714	0.494	1.694	0.471	1.673
12	42.5	203.7	68.8	134.9	10	12.4	69.2	0.840	0.513	1.710	0.380	1.580
13	51.4	255.1	84.8	170.3	11	16.0	85.1	0.930	0.500	1.699	0.294	1.468
14	51.0	306.1	103.0	203.1	12	18.2	71.4	0.854	0.352	1.547	0.173	1.238
15	53.0	359.1	126.8	232.3	13	23.8	·45.7	0.660	0.197	1.294	0.085	0.929
16	63.8	422.9	161.2	261.7	14	34.4	44.2	0.645	0.169	1.228	0.065	0.813
17	68.5	491.4	203.7	287.7	15	42.5	47.0	0.672	0.163	1.212	0.057	0.756
18	71.5	562.9	255.1	307.8	16	51.4	56.5	0.752	0.184	1.265	0.060	0.778
19	71.1	634.0	306.1	327.9	17	51.0	43.9	0.642	0.134	1.127	0.041	0.613
20	80.1	714.1	359.1	355.0	18	53.0	35.2	0.547	0.099	0.996	0.028	0.447
21	72.9	787.0	422.9	364.1	19	63.8	17.4	0.241	0.048	0.681	0.013	0.114

NOTES:

Col.3 = Cumulative Sum of Col.2.
Col.4 = Col.3 displaced by period of Moving Average.
Col.5 = Col.3 minus Col.4.
Col.6 = Col.1 displaced by half (period of Moving Average minus 1)
Col.7 = Col.2 displaced by period of Moving Average.

Col.8: First entry = $-2 \times 5.7 - 1 \times 6.9 + 1 \times 9.6 + 2 \times 11.6$.
Any subsequent entry = Previous entry + $3 \times$ Col.1 + $2 \times$ Col.7 − Col.5.

Col.9 = Log. Col.8, minus 1.
Col.10 = Col.8 divided by Col.5.
Col.11 = Log. Col.10 plus 2.
Col.12 = 100 times Col.10 divided by Col.5.
Col.13 = Log. Col.12 + 2.

TABLE A (continued) – COMMODITY A: CALCULATION OF TRENDS
PARABOLA AND SIMPLE MODIFIED EXPONENTIAL (by 3 point method) YEARS 10 to 21

		PARABOLA						SIMPLE MODIFIED EXPONENTIAL					
Year	Demand	a Factors		b Factors		c Factors		R Factors		S Factors		T Factors	
1	2	14	15	16	17	18	19	20	21	22	23	24	25
10	23·8	3,003	71471·4	−869	−20682·2	55	1309·0	1	23·8				
11	34·4	1,911	...	−451	...	25	...	1	...				
12	42·5	1,001	...	−111	...	1	...	1	...				
13	51·4	273	...	151	...	−17	...	1	...	1	51·4		
14	51·0	−273	...	335	...	−29	...	1	51·0	1	...		
15	53·0	−637	...	441	...	−35	...			1	...		
16	63·8	−819	...	469	...	−35	...			1	...		
17	68·5	−819	...	419	...	−29	...			1	...	1	68·5
18	71·5	−637	...	291	...	−17	...			1	71·5	1	...
19	71·1	−273	...	85	...	1	...					1	...
20	80·1	273	...	−199	...	25	...					1	...
21	72·9	1,001	72972·9	−561	−40896·9	55	4009·5					1	72·9

NOTES:

Cols. 14; 16; 18. Obtained from Table E (for 12 years).
Col. 15 = Col. 2 times Col. 14.
Col. 17 = Col. 2 times Col. 16.
Col. 19 = Col. 2 times Col. 18.
Col. 21 = Col. 2 times Col. 20.
Col. 23 = Col. 2 times Col. 22.
Col. 25 = Col. 2 times Col. 24.

PARABOLA:

a = Sum of Col. 15 divided by 4,004 (M in Table E).
a = 16·8909
b = Sum of Col. 17 divided by 4,004.
b = 8·9766
c = Sum of Col. 19 divided by 4,004.
c = −0·3367.

SIMPLE MODIFIED EXPONENTIAL:

R = Sum of Col. 21 divided by 5.
R = 40·620.
S = Sum of Col. 23 divided by 6.
S = 59·867.
T = Sum of Col. 25 divided by 5.
T = 72·820.

TABLE B – COMMODITY A: CALCULATION OF TRENDS
LOG PARABOLA AND GOMPERTZ (by 3 point method) YEARS 10 to 21

		LOG PARABOLA						GOMPERTZ					
Year	Log Demand	a Factors		b Factors		c Factors		R Factors		S Factors		T Factors	
1	26	27	28	29	30	31	32	33	34	35	36	37	38
10	1·3766	3,003	4133·93	-869	-1196·27	55	75·71	1	1·3766				
11	1·5366	1,911		-451		25		1					
12	1·6284	1,001		-111		1		1					
13	1·7110	273		151		-17		1		1	1·7110		
14	1·7076	-273		335		-29		1	1·7076	1			
15	1·7243	-637		441		-35				1			
16	1·8048	-819		469		-35				1			
17	1·8357	-819		419		-29				1		1	1·8357
18	1·8543	-637		291		-17				1	1·8543	1	
19	1·8519	-273		85		1						1	
20	1·9036	273		-199		25						1	
21	1·8627	1,001	1864·56	-561	-1044·97	55	102·45					1	1·8627

NOTES:
Col. 26 = Log Col.2.
Cols.27; 29; 31. Obtained from Table E (for 12 years).
Col. 28 = Col. 26 times Col.27.
Col. 30 = Col. 26 times Col.29.
Col. 32 = Col. 26 times Col.31.
Col. 34 = Col. 26 times Col.33.
Col. 36 = Col. 26 times Col.35.
Col. 38 = Col. 26 times Col.37.

LOG PARABOLA:
a = Sum Col. 28 divided by 4,004 (M from Table E).
a = 1·3284.
b = Sum Col. 30 divided by 4,004.
b = 0·10231.
c = Sum Col. 32 divided by 4,004.
c = −0·0048.

GOMPERTZ:
R = Sum Col. 34 divided by 5.
R = 1·59204.
S = Sum Col. 36 divided by 6.
S = 1·77295.
T = Sum Col. 38 divided by 5.
T = 1·86164.

TABLE C   63

TABLE C – COMMODITY A: CALCULATION OF TRENDS
LOGISTIC (3 point method) YEARS 10 to 21

Year	Reciprocal of Demand	R Factors		S Factors		T Factors	
1	39	40	41	42	43	44	45
10	0·0420	1	0·0420				
11	0·0291	1	· · · ·				
12	0·0235	1	· · · ·				
13	0·0195	1	· · · ·	1	0·0195		
14	0·0196	1	0·0196	1	· · · ·		
15	0·0189			1	· · · ·		
16	0·0157			1	· · · ·		
17	0·0146			1	· · · ·	1	0·0146
18	0·0140			1	0·0140	1	· · · ·
19	0·0141					1	· · · ·
20	0·0125					1	· · · ·
21	0·0137					1	0·0137

NOTES:
Col.39 = Reciprocal of Col.2.
Col.41 = Col.39 times Col.40.
Col.43 = Col.39 times Col.42.
Col.45 = Col.39 times Col.44.

LOGISTIC:
R = Sum of Col.41 divided by 5.
R = 0·02674
S = Sum of Col.43 divided by 6.
S = 0·01705
T = Sum of Col.45 divided by 5:
T = 0·01378.

TABLE D – FACTORS FOR FITTING THE LINEAR TREND
Demand = $a + bt$ $t = 1.$ for first year

NUMBER OF YEARS

a, b, Factors	5 (a)	5 (b)	6 (a)	6 (b)	7 (a)	7 (b)	8 (a)	8 (b)	9 (a)	9 (b)	10 (a)	10 (b)	11 (a)	11 (b)	12 (a)	12 (b)
Multiply 1st member of series by	8	−2	70	−15	+16	−3	42	−7	80	−12	66	−9	40	−5	286	−33
2nd	5	−1	49	−9	+12	−2	33	−5	65	−9	55	−7	34	−4	247	−27
3rd	2	0	28	−3	+8	−1	24	−3	50	−6	44	−5	28	−3	208	−21
4th	−1	1	7	3	+4	0	15	−1	35	−3	33	−3	22	−2	169	−15
5th	−4	2	−14	9	0	1	6	+1	20	0	22	−1	16	−1	130	−9
6th			−35	15	−4	2	−3	+3	5	+3	11	1	10	0	91	−3
7th					−8	3	−12	+5	−10	+6	0	3	4	1	52	+3
8th							−21	+7	−25	+9	−11	5	−2	2	13	+9
9th									−40	+12	−22	7	−8	3	−26	+15
10th											−33	9	−14	4	−65	+21
11th													−20	5	−104	+27
12th															−143	+33
Divide sum by M	10		105		28		84		180		165		110		858	

NUMBER OF YEARS

a, b, Factors	13 (a)	13 (b)	14 (a)	14 (b)	15 (a)	15 (b)	16 (a)	16 (b)	17 (a)	17 (b)	18 (a)	18 (b)	19 (a)	19 (b)	20 (a)	20 (b)
Multiply 1st member of series by	56	−6	130	−13	224	−21	170	−15	96	−8	646	−51	120	−9	266	−19
2nd	49	−5	115	−11	200	−18	153	−13	87	−7	589	−45	110	−8	245	−17
3rd	42	−4	100	−9	176	−15	136	−11	78	−6	532	−39	100	−7	224	−15
4th	35	−3	85	−7	152	−12	119	−9	69	−5	475	−33	90	−6	203	−13
5th	28	−2	70	−5	128	−9	102	−7	60	−4	418	−27	80	−5	182	−11
6th	21	−1	55	−3	104	−6	85	−5	51	−3	361	−21	70	−4	161	−9
7th	14	0	40	−1	80	−3	68	−3	42	−2	304	−15	60	−3	140	−7
8th	7	1	25	+1	56	0	51	−1	33	−1	247	−9	50	−2	119	−5
9th	0	2	10	+3	32	+3	34	+1	24	0	190	−3	40	−1	98	−3
10th	−7	3	−5	+5	8	6	17	+3	15	+1	133	+3	30	0	77	−1
11th	−14	4	−20	+7	−16	9	0	+5	6	+2	76	+9	20	+1	56	+1
12th	−21	5	−35	+9	−40	12	−17	+7	−3	+3	19	+15	10	+2	35	+3
13th	−28	6	−50	+11	−64	15	−34	+9	−12	+4	−38	+21	0	+3	14	+5
14th			−65	+13	−88	18	−51	+11	−21	+5	−95	+27	−10	+4	−7	+7
15th					−112	21	−68	+13	−30	+6	−152	+33	−20	+5	−28	+9
16th							−85	+15	−39	+7	−209	+39	−30	+6	−49	+11
17th									−48	+8	−266	+45	−40	+7	−70	+13
18th											−323	+51	−50	+8	−91	+15
19th													−60	+9	−112	+17
20th															−133	+19
Divide sum by M	182		455		840		680		408		2,907		570		1,330	

E

TABLE E – FACTORS FOR FITTING THE QUADRATIC TREND
Demand = $a + bt + ct^2$ $t = 1$ for first year of period

NUMBER OF YEARS	5 a	5 b	5 c	6 a	6 b	6 c	7 a	7 b	7 c	8 a	8 b	8 c
Multiply 1st member of series by	+126	−74	10	420	−215	+25	+108	−49	5	189	−77	7
2nd	0	+23	−5	84	11	−5	+36	−6	0	81	−19	1
3rd	−56	+60	−10	−112	132	−20	−12	+21	−3	3	21	−3
4th	−42	+37	−5	−168	148	−20	−36	+32	−4	−45	43	−5
5th	42	−46	+10	−84	59	−5	−36	+27	−3	−63	47	−5
6th				140	−135	+25	−12	+6	0	−51	33	−3
7th							+36	−31	+5	−9	1	1
8th										63	−49	7
Divide sum by M	70			280			84			168		

NUMBER OF YEARS	9 a	9 b	9 c	10 a	10 b	10 c	11 a	11 b	11 c	12 a	12 b	12 c
Multiply 1st member of series by	+4,620	−1,708	+140	+1,188	−402	30	+3,510	−1,095	+75	3,003	−869	55
2nd	+2,310	−581	+35	+660	−166	10	+2,106	−516	+30	1,911	−451	25
3rd	+550	246	−40	242	15	−5	+962	−57	−5	1,001	−111	1
4th	−660	773	−85	−66	141	−15	+78	282	−30	273	151	−17
5th	−1,320	1,000	−100	−264	212	−20	−546	501	−45	−273	335	−29
6th	−1,430	927	−85	−352	228	−20	−910	600	−50	−637	441	−35
7th	−990	554	−40	−330	189	−15	−1,014	579	−45	−819	469	−35
8th	0	−119	+35	−198	95	−5	−858	438	−30	−637	419	−29
9th	1,540	−1,092	+140	44	−54	10	−442	177	−5	−273	291	−17
10th				396	−258	30	234	−204	+30	273	85	1
11th							1,170	−705	+75	1,001	−199	25
12th											−561	55
Divide sum by M	4,620			1,320			4,290			4,004		

NUMBER OF YEARS	13			14			15			16		
a, b, c, Factors	a	b	c	a	b	c	a	b	c	a	b	c
Multiply 1st member of series by	+1,386	-374	+22	+4,680	-1,183	+65	+37,128	-8,827	+455	+16,065	-3,605	+175
2nd	+924	-209	+11	+3,240	-701	+35	+26,520	-5,486	+260	+11,781	-2,331	+105
3rd	+532	-72	+2	+2,000	-294	+10	+17,272	-2,625	+95	+8,007	-1,227	+45
4th	+210	+37	-5	+960	+38	-10	+9,384	-244	-40	+4,743	-293	-5
5th	-42	+118	-10	+120	+295	-25	+2,856	+1,657	-145	+1,989	+471	-45
6th	-224	+171	-13	-520	+477	-35	-2,312	+3,078	-220	-255	+1,065	-75
7th	-336	+196	-14	-960	+584	-40	-6,120	+4,019	-265	-1,989	+1,489	-95
8th	-378	+193	-13	-1,200	+616	-40	-8,568	+4,480	-280	-3,213	+1,743	-105
9th	-350	+162	-10	-1,240	+573	-35	-9,656	+4,461	-265	-3,927	+1,827	-105
10th	-252	+103	-5	-1,080	+455	-25	-9,384	+3,962	-220	-4,131	+1,741	-95
11th	-84	+16	+2	-720	+262	-10	-7,752	+2,983	-145	-3,825	+1,485	-75
12th	+154	-99	+11	-160	-6	+10	-4,760	+1,524	-40	-3,009	+1,059	-45
13th	462	-242	+22	600	-349	+35	-408	-415	+95	-1,683	+463	-5
14th				1,560	-767	+65	5,304	-2,834	260	+153	-303	+45
15th							12,376	-5,733	455	+2,499	-1,239	+105
16th										+5,355	-2,345	+175
Divide sum by M	2,002			7,280			61,880			28,560		

NUMBER OF YEARS	17			18			19			20		
a, b, c, Factors	a	b	c	a	b	c	a	b	c	a	b	c
Multiply 1st member of series by	4,104	-872	40	7,752	-1,564	68	32,130	-6,171	255	39,501	-7,239	285
2nd	3,078	-583	25	5,928	-1,076	44	24,990	-4,352	170	31,185	-5,217	195
3rd	2,166	-330	12	4,294	-645	23	18,550	-2,733	95	23,639	-3,405	115
4th	1,368	-113	1	2,850	-271	5	12,810	-1,314	30	16,863	-1,803	45
5th	684	68	-8	1,596	46	-10	7,770	-95	-25	10,857	-411	-15
6th	114	213	-15	532	306	-22	3,430	924	-70	5,621	771	-65
7th	-342	322	-20	-342	509	-31	-210	1,743	-105	1,155	1,743	-105
8th	-684	395	-23	-1,026	655	-37	-3,150	2,362	-130	-2,541	2,505	-135
9th	-912	432	-24	-1,520	744	-40	-5,390	2,781	-145	-5,467	3,057	-155
10th	-1,026	433	-23	-1,824	776	-40	-6,930	3,000	-150	-7,623	3,399	-165
11th	-1,026	398	-20	-1,938	751	-37	-7,770	3,019	-145	-9,009	3,531	-165
12th	-912	327	-15	-1,862	669	-31	-7,910	2,838	-130	-9,625	3,453	-155
13th	-684	220	-8	-1,596	530	-22	-7,350	2,457	-105	-9,471	3,165	-135
14th	-342	77	1	-1,140	334	-10	-6,090	1,876	-70	-8,547	2,667	-105
15th	114	-102	12	-494	81	5	-4,130	1,095	-25	-6,853	1,959	-65
16th	684	-317	25	342	-229	23	-1,470	114	30	-4,389	1,041	-15
17th	1,368	-568	40	1,368	-596	44	1,890	-1,067	95	-1,155	-87	45
18th				2,584	-1,020	68	5,950	-2,448	170	2,849	-1,425	115
19th							10,710	-4,029	255	7,623	-2,973	195
20th										13,167	-4,731	285
Divide sum by M	7,752			15,504			67,830			87,780		

TABLE F – FORECASTING: LINEAR TREND
90% CONFIDENCE LIMITS

Length of Series (n)	n + 1	n + 2	n + 3	n + 4	n + 5	n + 6	n + 7	n + 8	n + 9	n + 10	n + 11	n + 12	n + 13	n + 14	n + 15	Student's 't' 90%
5	2·468	3·158	3·866	4·586	5·313											2·353
6	1·985	2·454	2·936	3·426	3·921											2·132
7	1·703	2·051	2·408	2·773	3·139	3·510	3·883									2·015
8	1·514	1·786	2·065	2·351	2·639	2·930	3·221									1·943
9	1·376	1·597	1·825	2·056	2·291	2·524	2·765	3·004	3·242	3·483						1·895
10	1·270	1·455	1·644	1·838	2·033	2·228	2·427	2·626	2·827	3·026						1·860
11	1·186	1·342	1·503	1·668	1·833	2·000	2·168	2·339	2·508	2·680						1·833
12	1·114	1·250	1·390	1·531	1·674	1·819	1·964	2·111	2·258	2·406						1·812
13	1·056	1·176	1·297	1·421	1·546	1·674	1·801	1·929	2·058	2·188						1·796
14	1·007	1·112	1·219	1·329	1·440	1·552	1·664	1·778	1·892	2·007						1·782
15	0·962	1·057	1·153	1·250	1·350	1·450	1·551	1·652	1·753	1·856						1·771
16	0·923	1·009	1·095	1·183	1·273	1·363	1·453	1·544	1·636	1·728	1·821	1·914	2·008	2·101	2·194	1·761
17	0·889	0·966	1·045	1·125	1·206	1·287	1·369	1·451	1·536	1·620	1·702	1·786	1·872	1·956	2·040	1·753
18	0·859	0·929	1·000	1·074	1·147	1·222	1·297	1·372	1·447	1·524	1·601	1·678	1·755	1·832	1·908	1·746
19	0·832	0·896	0·962	1·028	1·096	1·164	1·232	1·302	1·371	1·441	1·512	1·582	1·653	1·723	1·794	1·740
20	0·806	0·865	0·926	0·987	1·049	1·111	1·176	1·240	1·302	1·368	1·432	1·496	1·562	1·626	1·692	1·734

NOTE:– In all columns except the first and the last, the numerical value in the heading means the number of years extrapolated, *e.g.* (*n* + 5) means the extrapolation is to 5 years ahead whatever the value of '*n*'.

TABLE G – FORECASTING : QUADRATIC TREND
90% CONFIDENCE LIMITS

Student's 't'

Length of series (n)	n + 1	n + 2	n + 3	n + 4	n + 5	n + 6	n + 7	n + 8	n + 9	n + 10	n + 11	n + 12	n + 13	n + 14	n + 15	90%
5	6·263	11·607	18·595	27·539	37·268											2·920
6	4·210	7·203	11·014	15·612	20·989											2·353
7	3·322	5·345	7·867	10·871	14·346	18·293	22·706									2·132
8	2·811	4·306	6·138	8·296	10·770	13·559	16·662									2·015
9	2·471	3·637	5·046	6·688	8·559	10·653	12·971	15·513	18·278	21·264						1·943
10	2·229	3·172	4·298	5·600	7·072	8·713	10·521	12·496	14·635	16·941						1·895
11	2·042	2·827	3·753	4·816	6·010	7·334	8·788	10·371	12·083	13·920						1·860
12	1·895	2·559	3·338	4·225	5·217	6·311	7·510	8·809	10·210	11·713						1·833
13	1·774	2·347	3·013	3·767	4·606	5·528	6·534	7·623	8·794	10·046						1·812
14	1·674	2·175	2·753	3·403	4·124	4·916	5·774	6·701	7·696	8·757						1·796
15	1·588	2·030	2·538	3·106	3·733	4·419	5·161	5·961	6·818	7·729						1·782
16	1·514	1·909	2·359	2·860	3·413	4·013	4·663	5·361	6·108	6·902	7·741	8·630	9·565	10·548	11·577	1·771
17	1·448	1·844	2·207	2·680	3·143	3·695	4·249	4·880	5·521	6·229	6·954	7·741	8·550	9·416	10·307	1·761
18	1·392	1·713	2·076	2·477	2·915	3·390	3·902	4·449	5·031	5·648	6·300	6·987	7·710	8·467	9·259	1·753
19	1·341	1·634	1·962	2·326	2·720	3·148	3·607	4·096	4·616	5·168	5·750	6·362	7·005	7·677	8·381	1·746
20	1·295	1·563	1·864	2·192	2·553	2·939	3·353	3·795	4·263	4·759	5·281	5·831	6·407	7·009	7·637	1·740

NOTE:– In all columns except the first and the last, the numerical value in the heading means the number of years extrapolated, e.g. (n + 5) means the extrapolation is to 5 years ahead whatever the value of 'n'.

TABLE H – TABLES OF THE GOMES *J* FUNCTION

for $n = 6$

r	$J(r)$ 6,1	$J(r)$ 6,2	$J(r)$ 6,3	$J(r)$ 6,4	$J(r)$ 6,5	$J(r)$ 6,6
0.00	0.0000	−4.0000	1.0000	1.0000	1.0000	1.0000
0.01	0.0409	−4.1015	0.9385	1.0397	1.0412	1.0412
0.02	0.0838	−4.2061	0.8738	1.0787	1.0849	1.0850
0.03	0.1287	−4.3140	0.8058	1.1170	1.1310	1.1316
0.04	0.1758	−4.4252	0.7343	1.1544	1.1797	1.1811
0.05	0.2252	−4.5398	0.6590	1.1908	1.2310	1.2337
0.06	0.2771	−4.6580	0.5800	1.2263	1.2850	1.2897
0.07	0.3317	−4.7800	0.4968	1.2606	1.3417	1.3493
0.08	0.3891	−4.9057	0.4093	1.2936	1.4011	1.4126
0.09	0.4495	−5.0354	0.3173	1.3252	1.4633	1.4800
0.10	0.5132	−5.1693	0.2206	1.3554	1.5284	1.5517
0.11	0.5803	−5.3073	0.1188	1.3838	1.5965	1.6279
0.12	0.6510	−5.4497	0.0118	1.4104	1.6675	1.7090
0.13	0.7256	−5.5967	−0.1007	1.4351	1.7415	1.7952
0.14	0.8043	−5.7483	−0.2191	1.4576	1.8186	1.8869
0.15	0.8873	−5.9047	−0.3435	1.4777	1.8989	1.9843
0.16	0.9751	−6.0661	−0.4744	1.4952	1.9824	2.0878
0.17	1.0678	−6.2326	−0.6120	1.5100	2.0691	2.1978
0.18	1.1657	−6.4045	−0.7567	1.5218	2.1590	2.3146
0.19	1.2693	−6.5818	−0.9089	1.5303	2.2523	2.4387
0.20	1.3788	−6.7647	−1.0688	1.5352	2.3490	2.5704
0.21	1.4947	−6.9534	−1.2370	1.5364	2.4491	2.7102
0.22	1.6172	−7.1480	−1.4138	1.5334	2.5527	2.8585
0.23	1.7469	−7.3488	−1.5997	1.5260	2.6597	3.0159
0.24	1.8842	−7.5560	−1.7951	1.5138	2.7703	3.1828
0.25	2.0295	−7.7696	−2.0005	1.4965	2.8844	3.3598
0.26	2.1834	−7.9899	−2.2164	1.4735	3.0020	3.5474
0.27	2.3463	−8.2170	−2.4433	1.4446	3.1232	3.7462
0.28	2.5189	−8.4512	−2.6817	1.4093	3.2479	3.9568
0.29	2.7017	−8.6927	−2.9322	1.3671	3.3762	4.1799
0.30	2.8953	−8.9415	−3.1955	1.3174	3.5080	4.4162
0.31	3.1005	−9.1980	−3.4721	1.2598	3.6433	4.6664
0.32	3.3179	−9.4622	−3.7627	1.1937	3.7821	4.9312
0.33	3.5482	−9.7344	−4.0679	1.1184	3.9243	5.2114
0.34	3.7923	−10.0148	−4.3886	1.0333	4.0698	5.5079
0.35	4.0510	−10.3035	−4.7253	0.9378	4.2186	5.8215
0.36	4.3251	−10.6007	−5.0790	0.8310	4.3705	6.1531
0.37	4.6156	−10.9066	−5.4504	0.7122	4.5255	6.5037
0.38	4.9235	−11.2213	−5.8403	0.5805	4.6833	6.8743
0.39	5.2497	−11.5451	−6.2497	0.4351	4.8439	7.2660
0.40	5.5955	−11.8780	−6.6795	0.2751	5.0070	7.6798
0.41	5.9619	−12.2203	−7.1306	0.0995	5.1725	8.1170
0.42	6.3502	−12.5721	−7.6040	−0.0929	5.3400	8.5788
0.43	6.7617	−12.9335	−8.1008	−0.3031	5.5094	9.0663
0.44	7.1977	−13.3046	−8.6221	−0.5323	5.6802	9.5811
0.45	7.6597	−13.6856	−9.1690	−0.7817	5.8523	10.1244
0.46	8.1491	−14.0765	−9.7427	−1.0527	6.0251	10.6978
0.47	8.6677	−14.4775	−10.3445	−1.3467	6.1982	11.3028
0.48	9.2170	−14.8886	−10.9756	−1.6652	6.3712	11.9411
0.49	9.7988	−15.3098	−11.6373	−2.0097	6.5436	12.6143

TABLE H (continued)

r	$J(r)$ 6,1	$J(r)$ 6,2	$J(r)$ 6,3	$J(r)$ 6,4	$J(r)$ 6,5	$J(r)$ 6,6
0.50	10.4150	−15.7412	−12.3311	−2.3818	6.7148	13.3242
0.51	11.0677	−16.1828	−13.0583	−2.7835	6.8842	14.0727
0.52	11.7588	−16.6346	−13.8206	−3.2164	7.0510	14.8618
0.53	12.4905	−17.0966	−14.6194	−3.6826	7.2146	15.6935
0.54	13.2651	−17.5686	−15.4564	−4.1841	7.3741	16.5699
0.55	14.0852	−18.0507	−16.3333	−4.7231	7.5286	17.4934
0.56	14.9531	−18.5425	−17.2518	−5.3020	7.6771	18.4661
0.57	15.8716	−19.0441	−18.2138	−5.9231	7.8185	19.4907
0.58	16.8435	−19.5551	−19.2210	−6.5890	7.9518	20.5698
0.59	17.8718	−20.0754	−20.2756	−7.3024	8.0757	21.7059
0.60	18.9595	−20.6046	−21.3794	−8.0661	8.1888	22.9019
0.61	20.1100	−21.1424	−22.5347	−8.8832	8.2896	24.1608
0.62	21.3266	−21.6885	−23.7436	−9.7569	8.3766	25.4856
0.63	22.6130	−22.2423	−25.0082	−10.6903	8.4481	26.8797
0.64	23.9729	−22.8033	−26.3311	−11.6871	8.5022	28.3463
0.65	25.4104	−23.3710	−27.7145	−12.7509	8.5370	29.8891
0.66	26.9295	−23.9448	−29.1610	−13.8855	8.5503	31.5116
0.67	28.5346	−24.5240	−30.6732	−15.0951	8.5399	33.2177
0.68	30.2303	−25.1076	−32.2536	−16.3839	8.5032	35.0116
0.69	32.0215	−25.6950	−33.9052	−17.7564	8.4378	36.8973
0.70	33.9131	−26.2851	−35.6307	−19.2173	8.3407	38.8793
0.71	35.9104	−26.8769	−37.4330	−20.7716	8.2089	40.9622
0.72	38.0190	−27.4692	−39.3152	−22.4245	8.0392	43.1507
0.73	40.2445	−28.0608	−41.2805	−24.1813	7.8281	45.4499
0.74	42.5932	−28.6503	−43.3319	−26.0479	7.5721	47.8649
0.75	45.0712	−29.2362	−45.4730	−28.0303	7.2670	50.4013
0.76	47.6853	−29.8169	−47.7070	−30.1346	6.9087	53.0647
0.77	50.4423	−30.3908	−50.0375	−32.3676	6.4927	55.8609
0.78	53.3496	−30.9558	−52.4682	−34.7361	6.0142	58.7963
0.79	56.4147	−31.5101	−55.0027	−37.2473	5.4681	61.8773
0.80	59.6456	−32.0513	−57.6450	−39.9088	4.8491	65.1104
0.81	63.0505	−32.5772	−60.3988	−42.7285	4.1512	68.5029
0.82	66.6381	−33.0853	−63.2684	−45.7147	3.3685	72.0619
0.83	70.4175	−33.5728	−66.2579	−48.8761	2.4943	75.7950
0.84	74.3981	−34.0369	−69.3715	−52.2218	1.5218	79.7102
0.85	78.5899	−34.4745	−72.6136	−55.7611	0.4436	83.8157
0.86	83.0030	−34.8822	−75.9887	−59.5041	−0.7481	88.1201
0.87	87.6484	−35.2565	−79.5015	−63.4611	−2.0616	92.6324
0.88	92.5371	−35.5938	−83.1567	−67.6428	−3.5057	97.3618
0.89	97.6810	−35.8899	−86.9590	−72.0606	−5.0895	102.3180
0.90	103.0923	−36.1406	−90.9135	−76.7262	−6.8230	107.5111
0.91	108.7836	−36.3414	−95.0253	−81.6520	−8.7166	112.9516
0.92	114.7684	−36.4874	−99.2995	−86.8508	−10.7812	118.6504
0.93	121.0604	−36.5735	−103.7413	−92.3360	−13.0285	124.6189
0.94	127.6741	−36.5943	−108.3564	−98.1214	−15.4708	130.8688
0.95	134.6245	−36.5441	−113.1501	−104.2218	−18.1211	137.4124
0.96	141.9274	−36.4166	−118.1281	−110.6521	−20.9931	144.2625
0.97	149.5990	−36.2055	−123.2961	−117.4283	−24.1013	151.4322
0.98	157.6564	−35.9040	−128.6601	−124.5668	−27.4609	158.9354
0.99	166.1173	−35.5047	−134.2261	−132.0848	−31.0882	166.7864
1.00	175.0000	−35.0000	−140.0000	−140.0000	−35.0000	175.0000

TABLE K – TABLES OF THE GOMES J FUNCTION

for $n = 7$

r	$J(r)$ 7,1	$J(r)$ 7,2	$J(r)$ 7,3	$J(r)$ 7,4	$J(r)$ 7,5	$J(r)$ 7,6	$J(r)$ 7,7
0.00	0.0000	−5.0000	1.0000	1.0000	1.0000	1.0000	1.0000
0.01	0.0512	−5.1321	0.9179	1.0394	1.0412	1.0412	1.0412
0.02	0.1050	−5.2686	0.8313	1.0774	1.0848	1.0850	1.0850
0.03	0.1616	−5.4097	0.7400	1.1140	1.1309	1.1316	1.1316
0.04	0.2211	−5.5555	0.6438	1.1489	1.1794	1.1811	1.1811
0.05	0.2838	−5.7062	0.5423	1.1821	1.2304	1.2337	1.2339
0.06	0.3499	−5.8620	0.4352	1.2133	1.2839	1.2896	1.2901
0.07	0.4196	−6.0232	0.3223	1.2423	1.3400	1.3491	1.3499
0.08	0.4932	−6.1899	0.2032	1.2689	1.3985	1.4124	1.4138
0.09	0.5709	−6.3623	0.0775	1.2929	1.4595	1.4796	1.4819
0.10	0.6531	−6.5408	−0.0551	1.3140	1.5230	1.5511	1.5546
0.11	0.7401	−6.7255	−0.1950	1.3320	1.5890	1.6270	1.6323
0.12	0.8322	−6.9166	−0.3427	1.3467	1.6574	1.7077	1.7153
0.13	0.9298	−7.1145	−0.4985	1.3576	1.7283	1.7934	1.8040
0.14	1.0332	−7.3194	−0.6631	1.3644	1.8016	1.8843	1.8989
0.15	1.1428	−7.5315	−0.8367	1.3669	1.8773	1.9809	2.0004
0.16	1.2592	−7.7512	−1.0201	1.3645	1.9553	2.0833	2.1091
0.17	1.3827	−7.9787	−1.2137	1.3569	2.0354	2.1919	2.2254
0.18	1.5139	−8.2143	−1.4181	1.3437	2.1178	2.3070	2.3500
0.19	1.6534	−8.4584	−1.6339	1.3244	2.2022	2.4289	2.4834
0.20	1.8017	−8.7112	−1.8619	1.2984	2.2885	2.5581	2.6264
0.21	1.9594	−8.9731	−2.1026	1.2652	2.3766	2.6949	2.7796
0.22	2.1272	−9.2444	−2.3568	1.2241	2.4664	2.8396	2.9438
0.23	2.3059	−9.5254	−2.6253	1.1747	2.5576	2.9927	3.1198
0.24	2.4961	−9.8165	−2.9088	1.1160	2.6501	3.1546	3.3084
0.25	2.6989	−10.1181	−3.2084	1.0475	2.7436	3.3257	3.5107
0.26	2.9149	−10.4305	−3.5248	0.9684	2.8380	3.5064	3.7276
0.27	3.1452	−10.7541	−3.8590	0.8776	2.9328	3.6972	3.9602
0.28	3.3909	−11.0893	−4.2120	0.7745	3.0277	3.8986	4.2097
0.29	3.6529	−11.4364	−4.5850	0.6578	3.1225	4.1110	4.4771
0.30	3.9326	−11.7959	−4.9790	0.5267	3.2166	4.3350	4.7640
0.31	4.2311	−12.1682	−5.3953	0.3799	3.3096	4.5711	5.0716
0.32	4.5499	−12.5536	−5.8350	0.2163	3.4011	4.8197	5.4015
0.33	4.8904	−12.9525	−6.2996	0.0344	3.4904	5.0815	5.7553
0.34	5.2541	−13.3654	−6.7904	−0.1670	3.5769	5.3570	6.1347
0.35	5.6429	−13.7926	−7.3089	−0.3895	3.6599	5.6468	6.5416
0.36	6.0583	−14.2346	−7.8568	−0.6347	3.7386	5.9514	6.9778
0.37	6.5025	−14.6917	−8.4355	−0.9044	3.8122	6.2714	7.4455
0.38	6.9775	−15.1644	−9.0469	−1.2004	3.8797	6.6075	7.9470
0.39	7.4856	−15.6530	−9.6929	−1.5246	3.9401	6.9602	8.4846
0.40	8.0291	−16.1578	−10.3753	−1.8793	3.9922	7.3301	9.0610
0.41	8.6106	−16.6793	−11.0961	−2.2667	4.0349	7.7179	9.6788
0.42	9.2329	−17.2177	−11.8576	−2.6893	4.0666	8.1242	10.3409
0.43	9.8989	−17.7733	−12.6620	−3.1497	4.0859	8.5496	11.0506
0.44	10.6119	−18.3465	−13.5116	−3.6506	4.0911	8.9947	11.8111
0.45	11.3753	−18.9375	−14.4091	−4.1951	4.0804	9.4601	12.6260
0.46	12.1926	−19.5465	−15.3569	−4.7865	4.0518	9.9463	13.4991
0.47	13.0679	−20.1736	−16.3579	−5.4280	4.0031	10.4540	14.4345
0.48	14.0054	−20.8190	−17.4150	−6.1235	3.9320	10.9837	15.4366
0.49	15.0095	−21.4828	−18.5312	−6.8769	3.8357	11.5358	16.5099

TABLE K (continued)

r	$J(r)$ 7,1	$J(r)$ 7,2	$J(r)$ 7,3	$J(r)$ 7,4	$J(r)$ 7,5	$J(r)$ 7,6	$J(r)$ 7,7
0.50	16.0851	−22.1649	−19.7098	−7.6923	3.7115	12.1110	17.6594
0.51	17.2373	−22.8653	−20.9542	−8.5742	3.5564	12.7095	18.8905
0.52	18.4718	−23.5838	−22.2678	−9.5274	3.3668	13.3317	20.2087
0.53	19.7945	−24.3201	−23.6545	−10.5571	3.1391	13.9781	21.6201
0.54	21.2116	−25.0740	−25.1180	−11.6687	2.8694	14.6487	23.1311
0.55	22.7301	−25.8449	−26.6626	−12.8681	2.5532	15.3438	24.7485
0.56	24.3573	−26.6323	−28.2924	−14.1615	2.1859	16.0634	26.4797
0.57	26.1008	−27.4354	−30.0120	−15.5554	1.7622	16.8074	28.3324
0.58	27.9692	−28.2534	−31.8261	−17.0571	1.2767	17.5757	30.3150
0.59	29.9712	−29.0852	−33.7395	−18.6741	0.7233	18.3679	32.4363
0.60	32.1166	−29.9295	−35.7574	−20.4144	0.0954	19.1835	34.7058
0.61	34.4154	−30.7849	−37.8852	−22.2866	−0.6142	20.0219	37.1336
0.62	36.8786	−31.6498	−40.1285	−24.2998	−1.4130	20.8821	39.7303
0.63	39.5179	−32.5221	−42.4931	−26.4638	−2.3094	21.7630	42.5075
0.64	42.3457	−33.3997	−44.9850	−28.7889	−3.3125	22.6633	45.4773
0.65	45.3753	−34.2801	−47.6108	−31.2862	−4.4320	23.5812	48.6526
0.66	48.6211	−35.1605	−50.3770	−33.9674	−5.6785	24.5148	52.0474
0.67	52.0981	−36.0376	−53.2904	−36.8450	−7.0633	25.4618	55.6764
0.68	55.8227	−36.9079	−56.3583	−39.9321	−8.5987	26.4192	59.5551
0.69	59.8120	−37.7674	−59.5881	−43.2430	−10.2981	27.3841	63.7004
0.70	64.0845	−38.6116	−62.9875	−46.7926	−12.1756	28.3527	68.1300
0.71	68.6600	−39.4355	−66.5646	−50.5968	−14.2468	29.3208	72.8628
0.72	73.5594	−40.2337	−70.3276	−54.6724	−16.5283	30.2837	77.9189
0.73	78.8052	−41.0001	−74.2853	−59.0375	−19.0379	31.2358	83.3198
0.74	84.4211	−41.7279	−78.4465	−63.7109	−21.7950	32.1712	89.0881
0.75	90.4326	−42.4097	−82.8205	−68.7129	−24.8204	33.0828	95.2481
0.76	96.8668	−43.0374	−87.4168	−74.0648	−28.1363	33.9630	101.8256
0.77	103.7525	−43.6020	−92.2453	−79.7894	−31.7667	34.8030	108.8479
0.78	111.1204	−44.0937	−97.3160	−85.9105	−35.7375	35.5933	116.3440
0.79	119.0032	−44.5017	−102.6395	−92.4536	−40.0763	36.3229	124.3450
0.80	127.4356	−44.8143	−108.2264	−99.4457	−44.8129	36.9800	132.8836
0.81	136.4548	−45.0187	−114.0878	−106.9152	−49.9791	37.5513	141.9947
0.82	146.1000	−45.1007	−120.2351	−114.8922	−55.6093	38.0219	151.7154
0.83	156.4131	−45.0453	−126.6799	−123.4086	−61.7402	38.3758	162.0850
0.84	167.4386	−44.8358	−133.4339	−132.4981	−68.4110	38.5950	173.1452
0.85	179.2237	−44.4541	−140.5094	−142.1963	−75.6640	38.6597	184.9404
0.86	191.8188	−43.8807	−147.9188	−152.5408	−83.5443	38.5482	197.5176
0.87	205.2771	−43.0944	−155.6745	−163.5714	−92.1002	38.2368	210.9267
0.88	219.6553	−42.0722	−163.7894	−175.3300	−101.3835	37.6992	225.2206
0.89	235.0136	−40.7891	−172.2765	−187.8607	−111.4495	36.9067	240.4555
0.90	251.4158	−39.2183	−181.1489	−201.2104	−122.3573	35.8281	256.6909
0.91	268.9298	−37.3306	−190.4199	−215.4282	−134.1701	34.4292	273.9899
0.92	287.6274	−35.0947	−200.1029	−230.5661	−146.9554	32.6724	292.4193
0.93	307.5848	−32.4766	−210.2112	−246.6787	−160.7853	30.5170	312.0500
0.94	328.8829	−29.4398	−220.7584	−263.8235	−175.7368	27.9185	332.9572
0.95	351.6074	−25.9449	−231.7578	−282.0614	−191.8921	24.8286	355.2202
0.96	375.8491	−21.9496	−243.2228	−301.4561	−209.3386	21.1947	378.9233
0.97	401.7042	−17.4083	−255.1666	−322.0748	−228.1699	16.9597	404.1557
0.98	429.2747	−12.2720	−267.6023	−343.9882	−248.4853	12.0613	431.0118
0.99	458.6685	−6.4881	−280.5426	−367.2706	−270.3911	6.4324	459.5913
1.00	490.0000	−0.0000	−294.0000	−392.0000	−294.0000	0.0000	490.0000

TABLE L – TABLES OF THE GOMES J FUNCTION

for $n = 8$

r	$J(r)$ 8,1	$J(r)$ 8,2	$J(r)$ 8,3	$J(r)$ 8,4	$J(r)$ 8,5	$J(r)$ 8,6	$J(r)$ 8,7	$J(r)$ 8,8
0.00	0.000	−6.000	1.000	1.000	1.000	1.000	1.000	1.000
0.01	0.062	−6.163	0.897	1.039	1.041	1.041	1.041	1.041
0.02	0.126	−6.331	0.789	1.076	1.085	1.085	1.085	1.085
0.03	0.195	−6.505	0.674	1.111	1.131	1.132	1.132	1.132
0.04	0.266	−6.686	0.553	1.144	1.179	1.181	1.181	1.181
0.05	0.342	−6.873	0.425	1.173	1.230	1.234	1.234	1.234
0.06	0.423	−7.066	0.290	1.200	1.283	1.290	1.290	1.290
0.07	0.507	−7.266	0.148	1.224	1.338	1.349	1.350	1.350
0.08	0.597	−7.474	−0.003	1.244	1.396	1.412	1.414	1.414
0.09	0.692	−7.689	−0.162	1.260	1.456	1.479	1.482	1.482
0.10	0.793	−7.912	−0.331	1.273	1.517	1.550	1.555	1.555
0.11	0.900	−8.144	−0.509	1.280	1.581	1.626	1.632	1.633
0.12	1.013	−8.384	−0.697	1.283	1.647	1.706	1.715	1.716
0.13	1.134	−8.633	−0.897	1.280	1.715	1.791	1.804	1.806
0.14	1.262	−8.891	−1.108	1.271	1.784	1.881	1.898	1.901
0.15	1.398	−9.159	−1.331	1.255	1.855	1.977	2.000	2.004
0.16	1.543	−9.437	−1.567	1.233	1.927	2.078	2.108	2.114
0.17	1.698	−9.726	−1.817	1.203	2.001	2.185	2.224	2.232
0.18	1.863	−10.026	−2.081	1.164	2.075	2.298	2.348	2.359
0.19	2.038	−10.337	−2.361	1.116	2.150	2.417	2.481	2.496
0.20	2.225	−10.660	−2.658	1.059	2.225	2.543	2.623	2.643
0.21	2.425	−10.996	−2.972	0.990	2.300	2.676	2.776	2.801
0.22	2.639	−11.345	−3.305	0.910	2.375	2.816	2.939	2.972
0.23	2.867	−11.707	−3.657	0.817	2.449	2.963	3.113	3.155
0.24	3.111	−12.084	−4.031	0.710	2.522	3.118	3.300	3.353
0.25	3.372	−12.475	−4.426	0.588	2.593	3.281	3.500	3.567
0.26	3.651	−12.881	−4.846	0.450	2.661	3.452	3.715	3.797
0.27	3.950	−13.303	−5.290	0.295	2.726	3.632	3.944	4.047
0.28	4.271	−13.742	−5.762	0.120	2.788	3.820	4.190	4.316
0.29	4.614	−14.198	−6.261	−0.076	2.844	4.018	4.453	4.606
0.30	4.982	−14.672	−6.791	−0.294	2.895	4.224	4.734	4.921
0.31	5.378	−15.164	−7.353	−0.536	2.940	4.440	5.035	5.261
0.32	5.802	−15.675	−7.949	−0.805	2.976	4.664	5.358	5.629
0.33	6.257	−16.206	−8.581	−1.102	3.004	4.899	5.703	6.027
0.34	6.747	−16.758	−9.252	−1.430	3.021	5.143	6.072	6.458
0.35	7.273	−17.331	−9.963	−1.792	3.025	5.397	6.466	6.925
0.36	7.839	−17.925	−10.718	−2.190	3.016	5.660	6.888	7.430
0.37	8.447	−18.543	−11.519	−2.627	2.992	5.932	7.339	7.978
0.38	9.102	−19.183	−12.369	−3.105	2.950	6.215	7.821	8.571
0.39	9.807	−19.848	−13.272	−3.632	2.887	6.506	8.337	9.214
0.40	10.567	−20.537	−14.229	−4.207	2.802	6.806	8.887	9.912
0.41	11.385	−21.251	−15.246	−4.835	2.692	7.114	9.475	10.667
0.42	12.267	−21.992	−16.325	−5.522	2.553	7.430	10.103	11.487
0.43	13.218	−22.759	−17.471	−6.272	2.382	7.753	10.773	12.376
0.44	14.244	−23.552	−18.688	−7.089	2.175	8.083	11.487	13.340
0.45	15.351	−24.373	−19.979	−7.980	1.929	8.417	12.250	14.386
0.46	16.546	−25.222	−21.350	−8.951	1.638	8.756	13.063	15.520
0.47	17.836	−26.099	−22.807	−10.007	1.298	9.097	13.930	16.751
0.48	19.230	−27.003	−24.353	−11.156	0.903	9.438	14.854	18.087
0.49	20.736	−27.936	−25.994	−12.404	0.447	9.779	15.838	19.536

TABLE L   75

TABLE L (continued)

r	$J(r)$ 8,1	$J(r)$ 8,2	$J(r)$ 8,3	$J(r)$ 8,4	$J(r)$ 8,5	$J(r)$ 8,6	$J(r)$ 8,7	$J(r)$ 8,8
0.50	22.363	−28.898	−27.737	−13.762	−0.076	10.115	16.886	21.108
0.51	24.123	−29.886	−29.588	−15.236	−0.674	10.446	18.001	22.814
0.52	26.025	−30.903	−31.553	−16.836	−1.354	10.767	19.187	24.666
0.53	28.083	−31.945	−33.639	−18.572	−2.126	11.075	20.448	26.676
0.54	30.310	−33.014	−35.854	−20.456	−2.998	11.366	21.789	28.857
0.55	32.720	−34.107	−38.205	−22.499	−3.982	11.635	23.213	31.224
0.56	35.328	−35.222	−40.701	−24.713	−5.088	11.878	24.725	33.794
0.57	38.153	−36.359	−43.351	−27.113	−6.330	12.087	26.330	36.583
0.58	41.211	−37.513	−46.162	−29.712	−7.720	12.256	28.031	39.610
0.59	44.524	−38.684	−49.146	−32.527	−9.275	12.378	29.834	42.895
0.60	48.114	−39.866	−52.312	−35.575	−11.009	12.444	31.744	46.461
0.61	52.002	−41.056	−55.671	−38.873	−12.942	12.444	33.765	50.331
0.62	56.217	−42.250	−59.233	−42.442	−15.092	12.367	35.903	54.532
0.63	60.785	−43.442	−63.012	−46.303	−17.482	12.201	38.161	59.091
0.64	65.737	−44.625	−67.018	−50.478	−20.134	11.932	40.546	64.039
0.65	71.105	−45.792	−71.265	−54.992	−23.073	11.545	43.063	69.410
0.66	76.926	−46.935	−75.767	−59.871	−26.329	11.022	45.714	75.238
0.67	83.238	−48.044	−80.536	−65.143	−29.930	10.345	48.506	81.563
0.68	90.083	−49.109	−85.589	−70.839	−33.910	9.492	51.443	88.428
0.69	97.508	−50.117	−90.939	−76.990	−38.305	8.439	54.528	95.876
0.70	105.560	−51.054	−96.604	−83.633	−43.154	7.160	57.766	103.959
0.71	114.295	−51.904	−102.599	−90.804	−48.500	5.625	61.158	112.730
0.72	123.769	−52.651	−108.941	−98.543	−54.390	3.802	64.708	122.246
0.73	134.047	−53.273	−115.649	−106.894	−60.873	1.654	68.417	132.571
0.74	145.196	−53.749	−122.740	−115.902	−68.004	−0.859	72.286	143.773
0.75	157.291	−54.055	−130.232	−125.617	−75.845	−3.782	76.315	155.925
0.76	170.411	−54.161	−138.146	−136.092	−84.459	−7.164	80.502	169.108
0.77	184.644	−54.037	−146.501	−147.382	−93.917	−11.059	84.844	183.408
0.78	200.083	−53.648	−155.317	−159.549	−104.296	−15.527	89.337	198.918
0.79	216.831	−52.957	−164.614	−172.657	−115.680	−20.636	93.973	215.739
0.80	234.997	−51.920	−174.413	−186.774	−128.157	−26.459	98.744	233.982
0.81	254.701	−50.490	−184.735	−201.976	−141.828	−33.076	103.639	253.764
0.82	276.071	−48.615	−195.601	−218.339	−156.796	−40.577	108.642	275.215
0.83	299.248	−46.237	−207.033	−235.949	−173.179	−49.059	113.737	298.472
0.84	324.381	−43.291	−219.050	−254.895	−191.100	−58.632	118.901	323.686
0.85	351.633	−39.707	−231.673	−275.272	−210.695	−69.413	124.108	351.019
0.86	381.181	−35.407	−244.923	−297.182	−232.109	−81.534	129.328	380.645
0.87	413.216	−30.304	−258.818	−320.733	−255.502	−95.137	134.524	412.755
0.88	447.941	−24.304	−273.378	−346.041	−281.044	−110.381	139.654	447.553
0.89	485.580	−17.303	−288.619	−373.227	−308.921	−127.437	144.667	485.259
0.90	526.372	−9.186	−304.558	−402.423	−339.331	−146.494	149.508	526.114
0.91	570.575	0.172	−321.208	−433.768	−372.493	−167.761	154.109	570.373
0.92	618.468	10.910	−338.581	−467.407	−408.638	−191.463	158.394	618.317
0.93	670.353	23.179	−356.688	−503.498	−448.018	−217.850	162.278	670.244
0.94	726.553	37.144	−375.534	−542.205	−490.906	−247.193	165.661	726.480
0.95	787.419	52.987	−395.122	−583.705	−537.595	−279.788	168.430	787.374
0.96	853.327	70.907	−415.453	−628.184	−588.400	−315.960	170.459	853.303
0.97	924.685	91.120	−436.519	−675.838	−643.661	−356.063	171.603	924.674
0.98	1001.929	113.863	−458.312	−726.877	−703.747	−400.483	171.700	1001.926
0.99	1085.532	139.396	−480.813	−781.520	−769.052	−449.642	170.568	1085.531
1.00	1176.000	168.000	−504.000	−840.000	−840.000	−504.000	168.000	1176.000

TABLE M – TABLES OF THE GOMES J FUNCTION

for $n = 9$

r	$J(r)$ 9,1	$J(r)$ 9,2	$J(r)$ 9,3	$J(r)$ 9,4	$J(r)$ 9,5	$J(r)$ 9,6	$J(r)$ 9,7	$J(r)$ 9,8	$J(r)$ 9,9
0.00	0.0000	−7.0000	1.0000	1.0000	1.0000	1.0000	1.0000	1.0000	1.0000
0.01	0.0718	−7.1933	0.8766	1.0388	1.0412	1.0412	1.0412	1.0412	1.0412
0.02	0.1476	−7.3936	0.7463	1.0749	1.0848	1.0850	1.0850	1.0850	1.0850
0.03	0.2275	−7.6010	0.6085	1.1081	1.1307	1.1316	1.1316	1.1316	1.1316
0.04	0.3118	−7.8160	0.4628	1.1381	1.1789	1.1810	1.1811	1.1812	1.1812
0.05	0.4010	−8.0389	0.3087	1.1646	1.2293	1.2336	1.2339	1.2339	1.2339
0.06	0.4954	−8.2699	0.1458	1.1872	1.2819	1.2895	1.2900	1.2901	1.2901
0.07	0.5954	−8.5096	−0.0266	1.2056	1.3365	1.3488	1.3499	1.3500	1.3500
0.08	0.7013	−8.7582	−0.2091	1.2193	1.3932	1.4118	1.4137	1.4139	1.4139
0.09	0.8137	−9.0162	−0.4021	1.2280	1.4517	1.4787	1.4818	1.4821	1.4822
0.10	0.9331	−9.2840	−0.6065	1.2312	1.5119	1.5497	1.5545	1.5550	1.5551
0.11	1.0599	−9.5620	−0.8229	1.2282	1.5738	1.6249	1.6320	1.6330	1.6331
0.12	1.1948	−9.8508	−1.0521	1.2187	1.6370	1.7047	1.7149	1.7164	1.7166
0.13	1.3383	−10.1507	−1.2948	1.2019	1.7014	1.7890	1.8034	1.8056	1.8060
0.14	1.4911	−10.4624	−1.5520	1.1772	1.7667	1.8783	1.8980	1.9013	1.9018
0.15	1.6540	−10.7863	−1.8246	1.1439	1.8327	1.9726	1.9991	2.0039	2.0047
0.16	1.8278	−11.1230	−2.1135	1.1011	1.8991	2.0722	2.1072	2.1139	2.1152
0.17	2.0132	−11.4731	−2.4198	1.0481	1.9656	2.1773	2.2227	2.2321	2.2339
0.18	2.2112	−11.8371	−2.7446	0.9839	2.0316	2.2880	2.3463	2.3590	2.3617
0.19	2.4228	−12.2158	−3.0890	0.9076	2.0968	2.4045	2.4784	2.4954	2.4992
0.20	2.6491	−12.6097	−3.4545	0.8180	2.1608	2.5270	2.6197	2.6422	2.6475
0.21	2.8913	−13.0196	−3.8423	0.7139	2.2228	2.6556	2.7708	2.8001	2.8074
0.22	3.1505	−13.4462	−4.2538	0.5941	2.2823	2.7905	2.9324	2.9702	2.9800
0.23	3.4283	−13.8902	−4.6907	0.4572	2.3386	2.9318	3.1051	3.1534	3.1665
0.24	3.7261	−14.3524	−5.1546	0.3017	2.3910	3.0795	3.2897	3.3509	3.3682
0.25	4.0456	−14.8336	−5.6472	0.1259	2.4384	3.2338	3.4869	3.5638	3.5864
0.26	4.3885	−15.3346	−6.1705	−0.0719	2.4799	3.3946	3.6977	3.7935	3.8228
0.27	4.7568	−15.8564	−6.7265	−0.2937	2.5145	3.5619	3.9228	4.0414	4.0791
0.28	5.1527	−16.3997	−7.3174	−0.5416	2.5408	3.7358	4.1633	4.3090	4.3571
0.29	5.5784	−16.9655	−7.9454	−0.8178	2.5576	3.9160	4.4199	4.5980	4.6589
0.30	6.0365	−17.5548	−8.6131	−1.1248	2.5634	4.1023	4.6938	4.9101	4.9867
0.31	6.5296	−18.1686	−9.3231	−1.4654	2.5563	4.2946	4.9859	5.2475	5.3432
0.32	7.0610	−18.8078	−10.0783	−1.8425	2.5346	4.4925	5.2974	5.6120	5.7310
0.33	7.6337	−19.4734	−10.8816	−2.2591	2.4961	4.6956	5.6294	6.0062	6.1532
0.34	8.2515	−20.1665	−11.7364	−2.7188	2.4386	4.9033	5.9830	6.4323	6.6130
0.35	8.9183	−20.8882	−12.6461	−3.2254	2.3595	5.1149	6.3595	6.8932	7.1143
0.36	9.6384	−21.6395	−13.6144	−3.7828	2.2559	5.3296	6.7601	7.3917	7.6610
0.37	10.4164	−22.4214	−14.6453	−4.3955	2.1248	5.5466	7.1861	7.9309	8.2576
0.38	11.2575	−23.2351	−15.7431	−5.0684	1.9625	5.7645	7.6388	8.5143	8.9090
0.39	12.1675	−24.0815	−16.9122	−5.8067	1.7652	5.9821	8.1196	9.1455	9.6205
0.40	13.1525	−24.9618	−18.1576	−6.6160	1.5287	6.1977	8.6298	9.8284	10.3982
0.41	14.2193	−25.8768	−19.4844	−7.5025	1.2481	6.4095	9.1708	10.5675	11.2486
0.42	15.3753	−26.8276	−20.8982	−8.4729	0.9184	6.6152	9.7440	11.3672	12.1788
0.43	16.6287	−27.8149	−22.4049	−9.5346	0.5335	6.8124	10.3506	12.2325	13.1967
0.44	17.9885	−28.8397	−24.0108	−10.6955	0.0872	6.9981	10.9921	13.1689	14.3113
0.45	19.4645	−29.9025	−25.7227	−11.9641	−0.4277	7.1689	11.6697	14.1821	15.5319
0.46	21.0675	−31.0040	−27.5479	−13.3499	−1.0191	7.3210	12.3847	15.2785	16.8693
0.47	22.8095	−32.1446	−29.4940	−14.8631	−1.6955	7.4500	13.1381	16.4646	18.3351
0.48	24.7034	−33.3244	−31.5692	−16.5147	−2.4667	7.5508	13.9309	17.7478	19.9421
0.49	26.7637	−34.5434	−33.7824	−18.3168	−3.3432	7.6177	14.7641	19.1359	21.7045

TABLE M (continued)

r	$J(r)$ 9,1	$J(r)$ 9,2	$J(r)$ 9,3	$J(r)$ 9,4	$J(r)$ 9,5	$J(r)$ 9,6	$J(r)$ 9,7	$J(r)$ 9,8	$J(r)$ 9,9
0.50	29.0060	−35.8014	−36.1428	−20.2824	−4.3366	7.6440	15.6382	20.6373	23.6378
0.51	31.4477	−37.0977	−38.6605	−22.4259	−5.4601	7.6224	16.5538	22.2610	25.7593
0.52	34.1078	−38.4313	−41.3459	−24.7625	−6.7277	7.5444	17.5108	24.0166	28.0878
0.53	37.0074	−39.8009	−44.2105	−27.3092	−8.1552	7.4004	18.5091	25.9147	30.6442
0.54	40.1695	−41.2043	−47.2661	−30.0842	−9.7602	7.1796	19.5480	27.9663	33.4514
0.55	43.6195	−42.6391	−50.5255	−33.1073	−11.5616	6.8696	20.6264	30.1834	36.5347
0.56	47.3853	−44.1020	−54.0000	−36.4000	−13.5808	6.4566	21.7424	32.5788	39.9219
0.57	51.4977	−45.5890	−57.7106	−39.9858	−15.8411	5.9250	22.8937	35.1663	43.6438
0.58	55.9905	−47.0950	−61.6658	−43.8899	−18.3683	5.2570	24.0769	37.9604	47.7342
0.59	60.9010	−48.6141	−65.8839	−48.1400	−21.1907	4.4329	25.2877	40.9768	52.2303
0.60	66.2701	−50.1390	−70.3819	−52.7661	−24.3397	3.4303	26.5208	44.2322	57.1732
0.61	72.1432	−51.6609	−75.1776	−57.8005	−27.8498	2.2240	27.7693	47.7442	62.6082
0.62	78.5699	−53.1698	−80.2901	−63.2785	−31.7591	0.7857	29.0252	51.5319	68.5850
0.63	85.6049	−54.6536	−85.7392	−69.2384	−36.1095	−0.9163	30.2782	55.6152	75.1587
0.64	93.3086	−56.0982	−91.5457	−75.7215	−40.9472	−2.9177	31.5165	60.0154	82.3898
0.65	101.7475	−57.4872	−97.7317	−82.7728	−46.3230	−5.2584	32.7256	64.7550	90.3449
0.66	110.9946	−58.8016	−104.3199	−90.4409	−52.2929	−7.9831	33.8885	69.8576	99.0977
0.67	121.1305	−60.0193	−111.3345	−98.7786	−58.9184	−11.1421	34.9850	75.3484	108.7290
0.68	132.2439	−61.1150	−118.8003	−107.8430	−66.2675	−14.7915	35.9914	81.2537	119.3283
0.69	144.4325	−62.0595	−126.7432	−117.6959	−74.4147	−18.9941	36.8802	87.6009	130.9938
0.70	157.8037	−62.8192	−135.1901	−128.4041	−83.4420	−23.8202	37.6189	94.4190	143.8340
0.71	172.4760	−63.3559	−144.1687	−140.0400	−93.4396	−29.3482	38.1703	101.7380	157.9682
0.72	188.5797	−63.6258	−153.7075	−152.6818	−104.5066	−35.6659	38.4907	109.5891	173.5281
0.73	206.2582	−63.5789	−163.8355	−166.4140	−116.7518	−42.8710	38.5301	118.0045	190.6585
0.74	225.6694	−63.1586	−174.5825	−181.3278	−130.2950	−51.0728	38.2305	127.0174	209.5194
0.75	246.9871	−62.3003	−185.9785	−197.5217	−145.2674	−60.3930	37.5256	136.6617	230.2865
0.76	270.4026	−60.9310	−198.0537	−215.1020	−161.8133	−70.9673	36.3390	146.9719	253.1538
0.77	296.1263	−58.9679	−210.8382	−234.1833	−180.0907	−82.9469	34.5832	157.9828	278.3347
0.78	324.3895	−56.3173	−224.3617	−254.8890	−200.2733	−96.5000	32.1582	169.7292	306.0644
0.79	355.4470	−52.8737	−238.6533	−277.3521	−222.5512	−111.8139	28.9499	182.2455	336.6018
0.80	389.5787	−48.5177	−253.7407	−301.7158	−247.1331	−129.0969	24.8282	195.5651	370.2322
0.81	427.0925	−43.1152	−269.6502	−328.1338	−274.2475	−148.5806	19.6450	209.7203	407.2695
0.82	468.3269	−36.5149	−286.4060	−356.7716	−304.1445	−170.5222	13.2319	224.7409	448.0596
0.83	513.6540	−28.5472	−304.0291	−387.8068	−337.0983	−195.2076	5.3978	240.6543	492.9829
0.84	563.4826	−19.0212	−322.5374	−421.4300	−373.4085	−222.9538	−4.0738	257.4837	542.4585
0.85	618.2621	−7.7230	−341.9441	−457.8455	−413.4033	−254.1128	−15.4284	275.2476	596.9475
0.86	678.4860	5.5870	−362.2569	−497.2722	−457.4414	−289.0749	−28.9435	293.9587	656.9573
0.87	744.6963	21.1774	−383.4771	−539.9445	−505.9146	−328.2726	−44.9326	313.6217	723.0461
0.88	817.4884	39.3483	−405.5984	−586.1127	−559.2514	−372.1850	−63.7497	334.2323	795.8283
0.89	897.5157	60.4354	−428.6047	−636.0447	−617.9193	−421.3429	−85.7939	355.7750	875.9794
0.90	985.4955	84.8135	−452.4693	−690.0260	−682.4289	−476.3333	−111.5149	378.2209	964.2424
0.91	1082.2148	112.9009	−477.1526	−748.3611	−753.3372	−537.8061	−141.4186	401.5253	1061.4346
0.92	1188.5372	145.1638	−502.6001	−811.3743	−831.2516	−606.4793	−176.0741	425.6242	1168.4541
0.93	1305.4097	182.1218	−528.7398	−879.4106	−916.8341	−683.1467	−216.1206	450.4318	1286.2884
0.94	1433.8708	224.3534	−555.4797	−952.8362	−1010.8061	−768.6852	−262.2757	475.8360	1416.0228
0.95	1575.0590	272.5021	−582.7048	−1032.0401	−1113.9531	−864.0627	−315.3444	501.6944	1558.8496
0.96	1730.2222	327.2833	−610.2735	−1117.4341	−1227.1301	−970.3473	−376.2283	527.8290	1716.0789
0.97	1900.7276	389.4920	−638.0140	−1209.4540	−1351.2673	−1088.7171	−445.9377	554.0210	1889.1497
0.98	2088.0729	460.0105	−665.7199	−1308.5603	−1487.3761	−1220.4710	−525.6024	580.0044	2079.6420
0.99	2293.8984	539.8179	−693.1454	−1415.2386	−1636.5556	−1367.0399	−616.4860	605.4585	2289.2906
1.00	2520.0000	630.0000	−720.0000	−1530.0000	−1800.0000	−1530.0000	−720.0000	630.0000	2520.0000

TABLE Q1 – 90% CONFIDENCE LIMITS OF MODIFIED EXPONENTIAL
$n = 5$

r \ f	1	2	3	4	5	6
0·50	3·138	3·651	3·976	4·171	4·284	4·349
0·55	3·386	4·108	4·614	4·949	5·163	5·298
0·60	3·650	4·631	5·382	5·927	6·309	6·572
0·65	3·928	5·221	6·298	7·146	7·792	8·273
0·70	4·221	5·884	7·381	8·652	9·697	10·535
0·75	4·527	6·623	8·649	10·496	12·124	13·527
0·80	4·847	7·442	10·124	12·737	15·198	17·461
0·85	5·181	8·346	11·829	15·443	19·063	22·604
0·90	5·528	9·338	13·789	18·687	23·890	29·285
0·95	5·888	10·423	16·030	22·554	29·880	37·904
1·0	6·263	11·607	18·595	27·539	37·268	48·688

TABLE Q2 – 90% CONFIDENCE LIMITS OF MODIFIED EXPONENTIAL
$n = 6$

r \ f	1	2	3	4	5	6
0·50	2·013	2·205	2·321	2·390	2·429	2·451
0·55	2·177	2·467	2·663	2·790	2·870	2·920
0·60	2·355	2·774	3·085	3·305	3·458	3·561
0·65	2·547	3·128	3·599	3·962	4·234	4·435
0·70	2·750	3·533	4·218	4·789	5·251	5·618
0·75	2·965	3·992	4·956	5·820	6·571	7·211
0·80	3·192	4·507	5·829	7·095	8·270	9·341
0·85	3·430	5·082	6·853	8·657	10·441	12·169
0·90	3·679	5·721	8·045	10·558	13·193	15·900
0·95	3·941	6·435	9·417	12·854	16·652	20·768
1·0	4·210	7·203	11·014	15·612	20·989	27·142

f = number of years extrapolated

TABLE N – TABLES OF THE GOMES *J* FUNCTION

for $n = 11$

r	$J(r)_{11,1}$	$J(r)_{11,2}$	$J(r)_{11,3}$	$J(r)_{11,4}$	$J(r)_{11,5}$	$J(r)_{11,6}$	$J(r)_{11,7}$	$J(r)_{11,8}$	$J(r)_{11,9}$	$J(r)_{11,10}$	$J(r)_{11,11}$
0.00	0.0000	-9.0000	1.0000	1.0000	1.0000	1.0000	1.0000	1.0000	1.0000	1.0000	1.0000
0.01	0.0925	-9.2546	0.8354	1.0381	1.0412	1.0412	1.0412	1.0412	1.0412	1.0412	1.0412
0.02	0.1901	-9.5186	0.6612	1.0723	1.0847	1.0850	1.0850	1.0850	1.0850	1.0850	1.0850
0.03	0.2933	-9.7924	0.4769	1.1022	1.1304	1.1316	1.1316	1.1316	1.1316	1.1316	1.1316
0.04	0.4025	-10.0766	0.2818	1.1272	1.1783	1.1810	1.1811	1.1812	1.1812	1.1812	1.1812
0.05	0.5182	-10.3715	0.0751	1.1470	1.2281	1.2335	1.2339	1.2339	1.2339	1.2339	1.2339
0.06	0.6409	-10.6778	-0.1437	1.1611	1.2798	1.2893	1.2900	1.2901	1.2901	1.2901	1.2901
0.07	0.7711	-10.9960	-0.3756	1.1689	1.3331	1.3485	1.3499	1.3500	1.3500	1.3500	1.3500
0.08	0.9094	-11.3265	-0.6213	1.1698	1.3879	1.4113	1.4137	1.4139	1.4139	1.4139	1.4139
0.09	1.0565	-11.6700	-0.8818	1.1632	1.4439	1.4779	1.4817	1.4821	1.4822	1.4822	1.4822
0.10	1.2130	-12.0272	-1.1579	1.1483	1.5009	1.5483	1.5543	1.5550	1.5551	1.5551	1.5551
0.11	1.3796	-12.3986	-1.4508	1.1244	1.5585	1.6228	1.6318	1.6329	1.6331	1.6331	1.6331
0.12	1.5573	-12.7850	-1.7615	1.0907	1.6165	1.7016	1.7144	1.7163	1.7166	1.7166	1.7166
0.13	1.7468	-13.1870	-2.0912	1.0462	1.6743	1.7846	1.8027	1.8055	1.8060	1.8060	1.8060
0.75	493.2585	-64.1148	-315.4089	-378.8276	-332.6027	-227.5923	-96.0783	42.1245	175.4519	297.7040	406.0855
0.76	549.9999	-55.6485	-337.5827	-416.3001	-373.1055	-261.9824	-118.0246	36.6066	188.4961	330.0530	457.4882
0.77	613.7586	-44.8863	-361.0497	-457.4307	-418.4041	-301.1590	-143.7403	29.1699	202.1180	365.9396	515.6840
0.78	685.4444	-31.4127	-385.8221	-502.5649	-469.0610	-345.7686	-173.8162	19.4184	216.2486	405.7397	581.5944
0.79	766.0878	-14.7445	-411.8960	-552.0781	-525.7034	-396.5438	-208.9321	6.8859	230.7899	449.8662	656.2682
0.80	856.8567	5.6796	-439.2471	-606.3766	-589.0307	-454.3144	-249.8696	-8.9764	245.6080	498.7715	740.8990
0.81	959.0746	30.5111	-467.8254	-665.9000	-659.8223	-520.0196	-297.5269	-28.8132	260.5254	552.9510	836.8454
0.82	1074.2413	60.5050	-497.5494	-731.1224	-738.9463	-594.7230	-352.9361	-53.3812	275.3113	612.9462	945.6547
0.83	1204.0568	96.5365	-528.2986	-802.5540	-827.3692	-679.6279	-417.2820	-83.5669	289.6701	679.3472	1069.0882
0.84	1350.4478	139.6182	-559.9050	-880.7427	-926.1665	-776.0953	-491.9247	-120.4083	303.2284	752.7962	1209.1519
0.85	1515.5985	190.9218	-592.1432	-966.2748	-1036.5340	-885.6646	-578.4244	-165.1191	315.5188	833.9902	1368.1307
0.86	1701.9843	251.8012	-624.7180	-1059.7755	-1159.8007	-1010.0757	-678.5700	-219.1168	325.9612	923.6836	1548.6265
0.87	1912.4112	323.8200	-657.2508	-1161.9093	-1297.4427	-1151.2947	-794.4120	-284.0555	333.8403	1022.6901	1753.6034
0.88	2150.0594	408.7831	-689.2629	-1273.3794	-1451.0978	-1311.5422	-928.2993	-361.8636	338.2799	1131.8847	1986.4380
0.89	2418.5337	508.7718	-720.1564	-1394.9262	-1622.5824	-1493.3254	-1082.9213	-454.7866	338.2121	1252.2044	2250.9763
0.90	2721.9191	626.1850	-749.1915	-1527.3246	-1813.9093	-1699.4737	-1261.3563	-565.4376	332.3408	1384.6479	2551.6002
0.91	3064.8453	763.7856	-775.4605	-1671.3809	-2027.3064	-1933.1789	-1467.1252	-696.8543	319.0996	1530.2745	2893.3012
0.92	3452.5582	924.7539	-797.8568	-1827.9269	-2265.2382	-2198.0395	-1704.2538	-852.5650	296.6601	1690.2003	3281.7658
0.93	3891.0017	1112.7479	-815.0397	-1997.8130	-2530.4279	-2498.1109	-1977.3427	-1036.6647	262.5838	1865.5936	3723.4720
0.94	4386.9095	1331.9732	-825.3927	-2181.8987	-2825.8817	-2837.9609	-2291.6464	-1253.9020	214.3340	2057.6667	4225.7989
0.95	4947.9096	1587.2612	-826.9756	-2381.0403	-3154.9144	-3222.7318	-2653.1636	-1509.7788	148.6171	2267.6645	4797.1522
0.96	5582.6413	1884.1592	-817.4693	-2596.0749	-3521.1769	-3658.2098	-3068.7389	-1810.6654	61.5796	2496.8492	5447.1060
0.97	6300.8883	2229.0332	-794.1108	-2827.8018	-3928.6860	-4150.9016	-3546.1779	-2163.9912	-51.3572	2746.4805	6186.5646
0.98	7113.7278	2629.1833	-753.6196	-3076.9571	-4381.8544	-4708.1200	-4094.3770	-2578.0954	-195.6222	3017.7885	7027.9461
0.99	8033.7004	3092.9773	-692.1116	-3344.1848	-4885.5241	-5338.0792	-4723.4713	-3062.9987	-377.6400	3311.9409	7985.3912
1.00	9075.0000	3630.0000	-605.0000	-3630.0000	-5445.0000	-6050.0000	-5445.000	-3630.0000	-605.0000	3630.0000	9075.0000

TABLE P — TABLES OF THE GOMES J FUNCTION

for n = 13

r	$J_{13,1}(r)$	$J_{13,2}(r)$	$J_{13,3}(r)$	$J_{13,4}(r)$	$J_{13,5}(r)$	$J_{13,6}(r)$	$J_{13,7}(r)$	$J_{13,8}(r)$	$J_{13,9}(r)$	$J_{13,10}(r)$	$J_{13,11}(r)$	$J_{13,12}(r)$	$J_{13,13}(r)$
0.00	0.000	-11.000	1.000	1.000	1.000	1.000	1.000	1.000	1.000	1.000	1.000	1.000	1.000
0.01	0.113	-11.316	0.794	1.037	1.041	1.041	1.041	1.041	1.041	1.041	1.041	1.041	1.041
0.02	0.233	-11.644	0.576	1.070	1.085	1.085	1.085	1.085	1.085	1.085	1.085	1.085	1.085
0.03	0.359	-11.984	0.345	1.096	1.130	1.132	1.132	1.132	1.132	1.132	1.132	1.132	1.132
0.04	0.493	-12.337	0.101	1.116	1.178	1.181	1.181	1.181	1.181	1.181	1.181	1.181	1.181
0.05	0.635	-12.704	-0.158	1.130	1.227	1.233	1.234	1.234	1.234	1.234	1.234	1.234	1.234
0.06	0.786	-13.086	-0.433	1.135	1.278	1.289	1.290	1.290	1.290	1.290	1.290	1.290	1.290
0.07	0.947	-13.482	-0.725	1.132	1.330	1.348	1.350	1.350	1.350	1.350	1.350	1.350	1.350
0.08	1.118	-13.895	-1.034	1.120	1.383	1.411	1.414	1.414	1.414	1.414	1.414	1.414	1.414
0.09	1.299	-14.324	-1.361	1.098	1.436	1.477	1.482	1.482	1.482	1.482	1.482	1.482	1.482
0.10	1.493	-14.770	-1.709	1.065	1.490	1.547	1.554	1.555	1.555	1.555	1.555	1.555	1.555
0.11	1.699	-15.235	-2.079	1.021	1.543	1.621	1.631	1.633	1.633	1.633	1.633	1.633	1.633
0.12	1.920	-15.719	-2.471	0.963	1.596	1.698	1.714	1.716	1.717	1.717	1.717	1.717	1.717
0.13	2.155	-16.223	-2.888	0.890	1.647	1.780	1.802	1.805	1.806	1.806	1.806	1.806	1.806
0.14	2.407	-16.749	-3.330	0.803	1.697	1.866	1.896	1.901	1.902	1.902	1.902	1.902	1.902
0.15	2.677	-17.296	-3.801	0.698	1.743	1.956	1.996	2.003	2.005	2.005	2.005	2.005	2.005
0.16	2.965	-17.867	-4.301	0.574	1.786	2.050	2.103	2.113	2.115	2.115	2.115	2.115	2.115
0.17	3.274	-18.462	-4.833	0.430	1.825	2.147	2.217	2.231	2.234	2.234	2.234	2.234	2.234
0.18	3.606	-19.084	-5.399	0.263	1.858	2.249	2.338	2.357	2.361	2.362	2.362	2.362	2.362
0.19	3.962	-19.732	-6.001	0.073	1.885	2.354	2.467	2.493	2.499	2.500	2.500	2.500	2.500
0.20	4.345	-20.409	-6.642	-0.145	1.903	2.462	2.604	2.639	2.647	2.649	2.649	2.649	2.649
0.21	4.756	-21.115	-7.325	-0.392	1.912	2.574	2.750	2.795	2.806	2.809	2.810	2.810	2.810
0.22	5.198	-21.853	-8.052	-0.670	1.910	2.688	2.905	2.963	2.978	2.982	2.983	2.983	2.983
0.23	5.675	-22.624	-8.827	-0.983	1.895	2.804	3.070	3.144	3.164	3.169	3.171	3.171	3.171
0.24	6.188	-23.430	-9.654	-1.335	1.865	2.921	3.244	3.338	3.365	3.372	3.374	3.375	3.375
0.25	6.742	-24.273	-10.535	-1.728	1.817	3.039	3.429	3.547	3.582	3.592	3.595	3.596	3.596
0.26	7.340	-25.153	-11.475	-2.166	1.750	3.157	3.624	3.772	3.817	3.830	3.834	3.835	3.836
0.27	7.987	-26.074	-12.479	-2.655	1.659	3.273	3.830	4.013	4.071	4.089	4.095	4.096	4.097
0.28	8.685	-27.038	-13.551	-3.198	1.543	3.386	4.046	4.272	4.346	4.370	4.378	4.380	4.381
0.29	9.441	-28.046	-14.696	-3.800	1.397	3.494	4.274	4.550	4.644	4.676	4.686	4.689	4.691
0.30	10.260	-29.101	-15.919	-4.468	1.216	3.596	4.513	4.848	4.967	5.008	5.022	5.027	5.029
0.31	11.148	-30.205	-17.228	-5.208	0.998	3.690	4.762	5.169	5.318	5.371	5.390	5.396	5.398
0.32	12.112	-31.360	-18.627	-6.026	0.735	3.772	5.023	5.512	5.698	5.766	5.791	5.800	5.803
0.33	13.158	-32.570	-20.124	-6.929	0.423	3.839	5.293	5.881	6.110	6.198	6.230	6.243	6.247
0.34	14.295	-33.836	-21.726	-7.927	0.056	3.889	5.573	6.275	6.558	6.669	6.712	6.728	6.734
0.35	15.533	-35.162	-23.442	-9.029	-0.375	3.917	5.862	6.697	7.044	7.184	7.240	7.261	7.270
0.36	16.881	-36.550	-25.281	-10.243	-0.876	3.919	6.158	7.148	7.571	7.747	7.819	7.848	7.860
0.37	18.351	-38.003	-27.252	-11.582	-1.458	3.889	6.459	7.629	8.143	8.364	8.456	8.494	8.510
0.38	19.954	-39.524	-29.366	-13.058	-2.130	3.820	6.764	8.142	8.765	9.039	9.157	9.207	9.229
0.39	21.706	-41.115	-31.634	-14.683	-2.904	3.706	7.070	8.688	9.439	9.779	9.929	9.995	10.023
0.40	23.622	-42.780	-34.068	-16.473	-3.792	3.538	7.373	9.269	10.171	10.590	10.781	10.866	10.904
0.41	25.718	-44.522	-36.682	-18.445	-4.809	3.307	7.670	9.884	10.965	11.480	11.720	11.831	11.881
0.42	28.016	-46.344	-39.490	-20.615	-5.970	3.003	7.956	10.535	11.826	12.457	12.758	12.901	12.967
0.43	30.537	-48.247	-42.508	-23.005	-7.294	2.611	8.225	11.221	12.760	13.529	13.907	14.089	14.176
0.44	33.305	-50.235	-45.753	-25.637	-8.802	2.119	8.469	11.944	13.772	14.708	15.177	15.410	15.523

TABLE Q3 – 90% CONFIDENCE LIMITS OF MODIFIED EXPONENTIAL
n = 7

r \ f	1	2	3	4	5	6	7
0·50	1·520	1·604	1·653	1·682	1·698	1·707	1·712
0·55	1·645	1·782	1·872	1·930	1·966	1·988	2·001
0·60	1·784	1·996	2·150	2·257	2·330	2·379	2·411
0·65	1·937	2·249	2·495	2·682	2·821	2·922	2·995
0·70	2·102	2·543	2·920	3·230	3·477	3·672	3·823
0·75	2·278	2·882	3·436	3·925	4·345	4·700	4·995
0·80	2·466	3·268	4·056	4·799	5·482	6·098	6·646
0·85	2·665	3·704	4·793	5·887	6·957	7·984	8·956
0·90	2·874	4·193	5·663	7·229	8·855	10·509	12·171
0·95	3·093	4·739	6·682	8·873	11·277	13·866	16·612
1·0	3·322	5·345	7·867	10·871	14·346	18·293	22·706

TABLE Q4 – 90% CONFIDENCE LIMITS OF MODIFIED EXPONENTIAL
n = 8

r \ f	1	2	3	4	5	6	7	8
0·50	1·235	1·274	1·296	1·309	1·316	1·320	1·322	1·324
0·55	1·335	1·405	1·449	1·477	1·495	1·505	1·511	1·515
0·60	1·450	1·566	1·647	1·704	1·742	1·767	1·784	1·794
0·65	1·578	1·760	1·900	2·005	2·082	2·137	2·177	2·205
0·70	1·721	1·991	2·217	2·400	2·545	2·658	2·746	2·812
0·75	1·875	2·262	2·610	2·912	3·170	3·386	3·565	3·711
0·80	2·041	2·574	3·088	3·567	4·003	4·393	4·737	5·040
0·85	2·218	2·932	3·666	4·395	5·100	5·773	6·406	6·996
0·90	2·406	3·337	4·357	5·430	6·534	7·649	8·762	9·862
0·95	2·603	3·794	5·175	6·714	8·389	10·178	12·066	14·037
1·0	2·811	4·306	6·138	8·296	10·770	13·559	16·662	20·078

f = number of years extrapolated

TABLE Q5 – 90% CONFIDENCE LIMITS OF MODIFIED EXPONENTIAL
$n = 9$

r \ f	1	2	3	4	5	6	7	8	9
0·50	1·049	1·066	1·077	1·083	1·086	1·088	1·089	1·090	1·090
0·55	1·130	1·166	1·189	1·204	1·212	1·218	1·221	1·223	1·224
0·60	1·226	1·292	1·338	1·369	1·390	1·403	1·412	1·418	1·422
0·65	1·338	1·448	1·532	1·593	1·638	1·670	1·693	1·709	1·720
0·70	1·464	1·638	1·780	1·894	1·984	2·053	2·106	2·146	2·177
0·75	1·603	1·863	2·094	2·292	2·459	2·598	2·712	2·805	2·881
0·80	1·755	2·128	2·482	2·809	3·103	3·364	3·595	3·795	3·969
0·85	1·918	2·435	2·958	3·472	3·966	4·433	4·870	5·276	5·650
0·90	2·093	2·787	3·535	4·314	5·109	5·907	6·700	7·479	8·240
0·95	2·277	3·186	4·225	5·372	6·609	7·923	9·302	10·736	12·215
1·0	2·471	3·637	5·046	6·688	8·559	10·653	12·971	15·513	18·278

TABLE Q6 – 90% CONFIDENCE LIMITS OF MODIFIED EXPONENTIAL
$n = 10$

r \ f	1	2	3	4	5	6	7	8	9	10
0·50	0·915	0·925	0·930	0·933	0·934	0·935	0·936	0·936	0·936	0·936
0·55	0·983	1·003	1·015	1·023	1·027	1·030	1·032	1·033	1·033	1·033
0·60	1·066	1·105	1·131	1·148	1·160	1·167	1·172	1·175	1·177	1·179
0·65	1·164	1·233	1·284	1·322	1·348	1·367	1·381	1·390	1·397	1·402
0·70	1·278	1·392	1·485	1·559	1·616	1·660	1·693	1·718	1·737	1·752
0·75	1·405	1·586	1·744	1·878	1·990	2·083	2·159	2·221	2·271	2·311
0·80	1·547	1·817	2·070	2·300	2·507	2·690	2·850	2·989	3·108	3·211
0·85	1·700	2·088	2·476	2·852	3·212	3·550	3·865	4·156	4·423	4·667
0·90	1·866	2·402	2·973	3·562	4·158	4·754	5·343	5·919	6·480	7·023
0·95	2·042	2·762	3·575	4·464	5·417	6·423	7·474	8·563	9·682	10·827
1·0	2·229	3·172	4·298	5·600	7·072	8·713	10·521	12·496	14·635	16·941

f = number of years extrapolated

TABLE Q7 – 90% CONFIDENCE LIMITS OF MODIFIED EXPONENTIAL
$n = 11$

r \ f	1	2	3	4	5	6	7	8	9	10
0·50	0·817	0·822	0·824	0·826	0·827	0·827	0·827	0·827	0·827	0·827
0·55	0·874	0·885	0·891	0·895	0·898	0·899	0·900	0·900	0·901	0·901
0·60	0·945	0·968	0·983	0·993	0·999	1·004	1·007	1·008	1·009	1·010
0·65	1·032	1·075	1·107	1·130	1·147	1·158	1·166	1·172	1·176	1·179
0·70	1·134	1·212	1·273	1·322	1·359	1·387	1·409	1·425	1·438	1·447
0·75	1·252	1·381	1·491	1·585	1·662	1·726	1·778	1·820	1·853	1·880
0·80	1·385	1·586	1·772	1·938	2·088	2·219	2·334	2·432	2·517	2·590
0·85	1·532	1·830	2·125	2·409	2·678	2·931	3·164	3·380	3·576	3·755
0·90	1·691	2·116	2·564	3·022	3·483	3·941	4·392	4·832	5·259	5·670
0·95	1·861	2·447	3·101	3·811	4·567	5·361	6·188	7·041	7·915	8·807
1·0	2·042	2·827	3·753	4·816	6·010	7·334	8·788	10·371	12·083	13·920

TABLE Q8 – 90% CONFIDENCE LIMITS OF MODIFIED EXPONENTIAL
$n = 12$

r \ f	1	2	3	4	5	6	7	8	9	10
0·50	0·742	0·744	0·745	0·746	0·746	0·746	0·746	0·746	0·746	0·746
0·55	0·789	0·795	0·799	0·801	0·802	0·803	0·803	0·803	0·804	0·804
0·60	0·850	0·864	0·873	0·878	0·882	0·885	0·886	0·887	0·888	0·888
0·65	0·927	0·955	0·975	0·989	1·000	1·007	1·012	1·015	1·018	1·019
0·70	1·020	1·073	1·114	1·147	1·172	1·190	1·205	1·215	1·223	1·229
0·75	1·130	1·222	1·301	1·367	1·422	1·466	1·502	1·531	1·555	1·573
0·80	1·256	1·407	1·546	1·670	1·780	1·876	1·959	2·031	2·093	2·145
0·85	1·396	1·630	1·859	2·078	2·284	2·477	2·654	2·817	2·965	3·100
0·90	1·550	1·894	2·253	2·617	2·982	3·343	3·696	4·040	4·372	4·692
0·95	1·717	2·203	2·741	3·320	3·934	4·576	5·242	5·926	6·626	7·338
1·0	1·895	2·559	3·338	4·225	5·217	6·311	7·510	8·809	10·210	11·713

f = number of years extrapolated

F

TABLE Q9 – 90% CONFIDENCE LIMITS OF MODIFIED EXPONENTIAL
$n = 13$

r \ f	1	2	3	4	5	6	7	8	9	10
0·50	0·682	0·683	0·683	0·684	0·684	0·684	0·684	0·684	0·684	00·684
0·55	0·722	0·725	0·727	0·728	0·729	0·729	0·729	0·730	0·730	0·730
0·60	0·775	0·783	0·788	0·791	0·794	0·795	0·796	0·796	0·797	00·797
0·65	0·842	0·860	0·873	0·882	0·889	0·893	0·896	0·899	0·900	0·901
0·70	0·927	0·963	0·992	1·014	1·030	1·043	1·052	1·060	1·065	1·069
0·75	1·029	1·097	1·154	1·201	1·240	1·272	1·297	1·318	1·334	1·347
0·80	1·149	1·265	1·370	1·464	1·546	1·618	1·679	1·733	1·778	1·816
0·85	1·285	1·471	1·652	1·823	1·984	2·133	2·270	2·396	2·510	2·613
0·90	1·435	1·718	2·010	2·305	2·599	2·888	3·170	3·444	3·708	3·962
0·95	1·598	2·008	2·458	2·940	3·448	3·977	4·524	5·084	5·656	6·235
1·0	1·774	2·347	3·013	3·767	4·606	5·528	6·534	7·623	8·794	10·046

TABLE Q10 – 90% CONFIDENCE LIMITS OF MODIFIED EXPONENTIAL
$n = 14$

r \ f	1	2	3	4	5	6	7	8	9	10
0·50	0·633	0·634	0·634	0·634	0·635	0·635	0·635	0·635	0·635	0·635
0·55	0·668	0·669	0·671	0·671	0·672	0·672	0·672	0·672	0·672	0·672
0·60	0·713	0·718	0·721	0·723	0·725	0·725	0·726	0·726	0·727	0·727
0·65	0·773	0·785	0·793	0·799	0·803	0·806	0·808	0·809	0·810	0·811
0·70	0·850	0·876	0·895	0·910	0·921	0·930	0·936	0·941	0·945	0·947
0·75	0·946	0·996	1·037	1·072	1·100	1·122	1·140	1·155	1·166	1·176
0·80	1·060	1·150	1·230	1·302	1·364	1·418	1·465	1·504	1·538	1·567
0·85	1·191	1·341	1·486	1·622	1·749	1·867	1·974	2·072	2·161	2·242
0·90	1·338	1·574	1·815	2·058	2·298	2·534	2·763	2·985	3·198	3·402
0·95	1·499	1·851	2·232	2·639	3·066	3·509	3·965	4·432	4·906	5·386
1·0	1·674	2·175	2·753	3·403	4·124	4·916	5·774	6·701	7·696	8·757

f = number of years extrapolated

TABLE Q11 – 90% CONFIDENCE LIMITS OF MODIFIED EXPONENTIAL
$n = 15$

r \ f	1	2	3	4	5	6	7	8	9	10
0·50	0·593	0·594	0·594	0·594	0·594	0·594	0·594	0·594	0·594	0·594
0·55	0·623	0·624	0·624	0·625	0·625	0·625	0·625	0·625	0·625	0·625
0·60	0·662	0·665	0·667	0·668	0·669	0·669	0·670	0·670	0·670	0·670
0·65	0·715	0·723	0·728	0·732	0·735	0·736	0·738	0·739	0·739	0·740
0·70	0·785	0·803	0·817	0·827	0·835	0·840	0·845	0·848	0·850	0·852
0·75	0·874	0·911	0·942	0·967	0·987	1·004	1·017	1·027	1·035	1·042
0·80	0·983	1·053	1·116	1·170	1·218	1·259	1·295	1·325	1·349	1·372
0·85	1·110	1·233	1·349	1·459	1·560	1·654	1·739	1·817	1·887	1·950
0·90	1·255	1·453	1·655	1·856	2·055	2·249	2·438	2·619	2·794	2·961
0·95	1·414	1·718	2·046	2·393	2·756	3·132	3·517	3·910	4·310	4·713
1·0	1·588	2·030	2·538	3·106	3·733	4·419	5·161	5·961	6·818	7·729

f = number of years extrapolated

GRAPH A

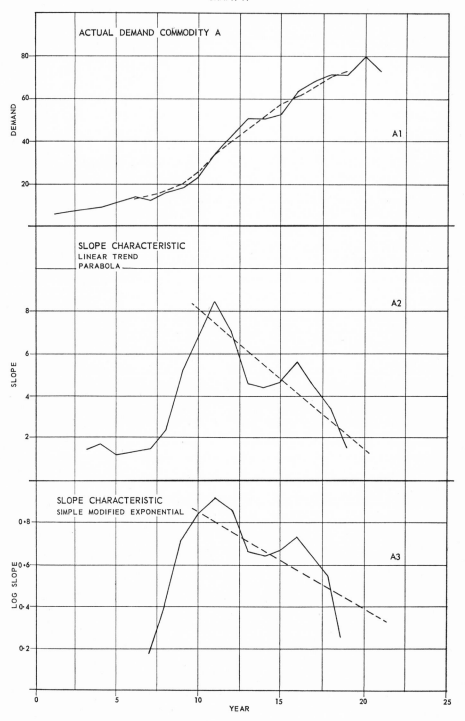

ACTUAL DEMAND COMMODITY A

A1

SLOPE CHARACTERISTIC
LINEAR TREND
PARABOLA

A2

SLOPE CHARACTERISTIC
SIMPLE MODIFIED EXPONENTIAL

A3

YEAR

GRAPH B

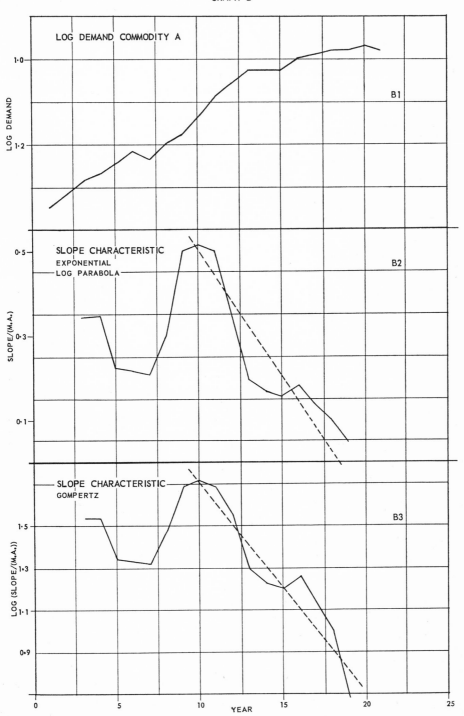

GRAPH C

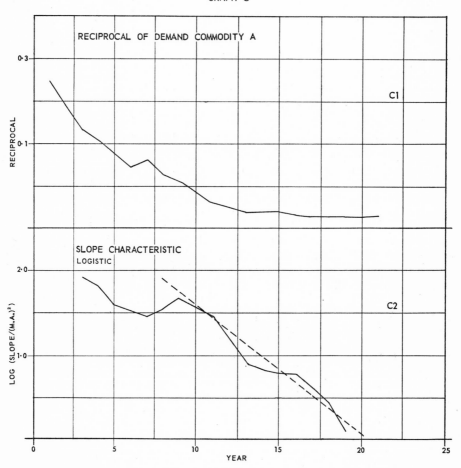

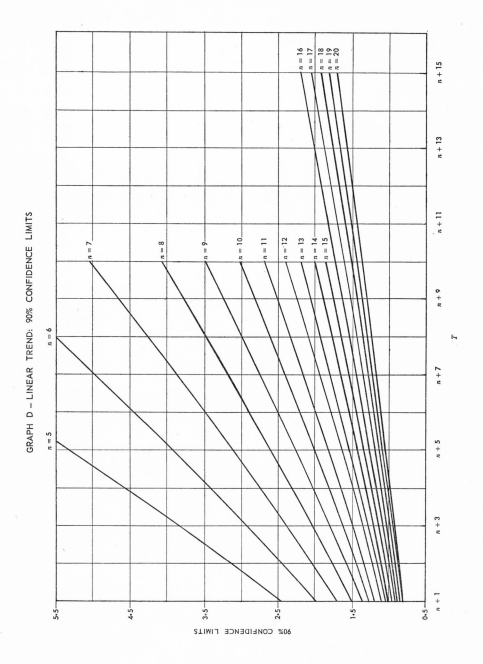

GRAPH D – LINEAR TREND: 90% CONFIDENCE LIMITS

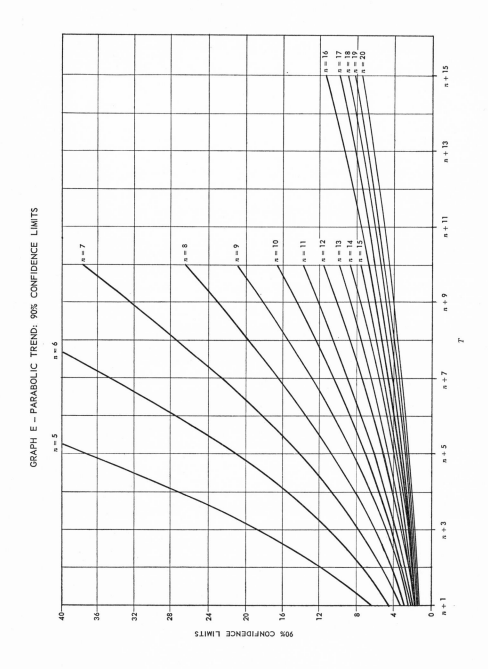

GRAPH E – PARABOLIC TREND: 90% CONFIDENCE LIMITS

GRAPH F1 – 90% CONFIDENCE LIMITS OF MODIFIED EXPONENTIAL

$n = 5$

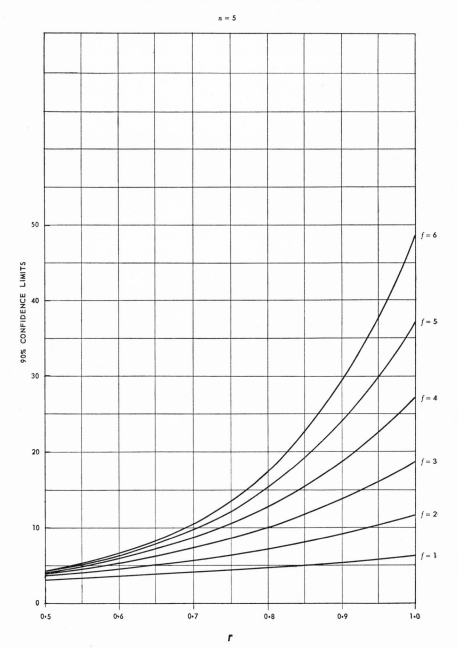

GRAPH F2 – 90% CONFIDENCE LIMITS OF MODIFIED EXPONENTIAL

$n = 6$

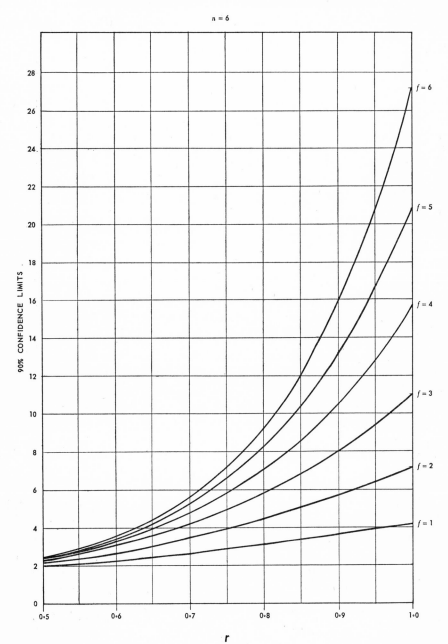

GRAPH F3 – 90% CONFIDENCE LIMITS OF MODIFIED EXPONENTIAL

$n = 7$

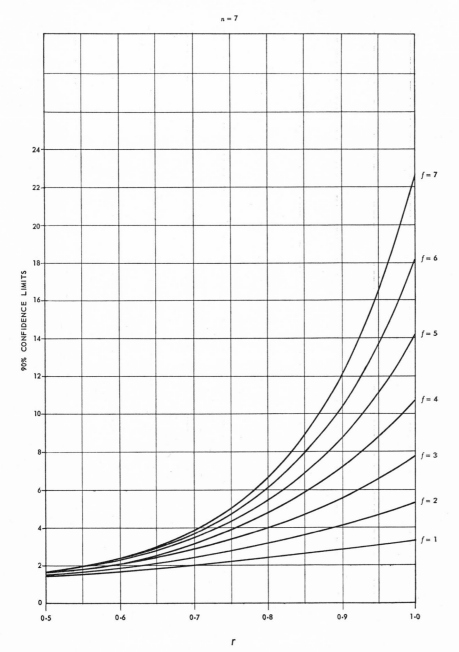

GRAPH F4 – 90% CONFIDENCE LIMITS OF MODIFIED EXPONENTIAL

$n = 8$

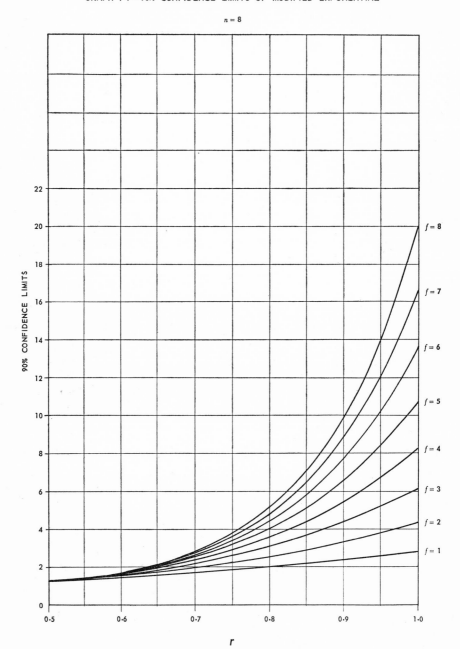

GRAPH F5 – 90% CONFIDENCE LIMITS OF MODIFIED EXPONENTIAL

$n = 9$

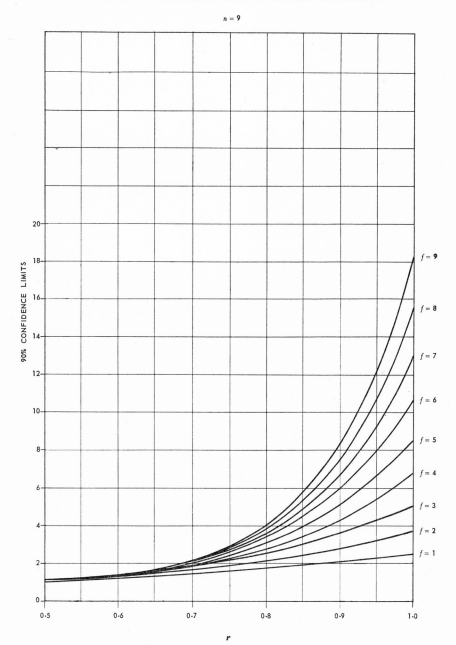

GRAPH F6 – 90% CONFIDENCE LIMITS OF MODIFIED EXPONENTIAL

$n = 10$

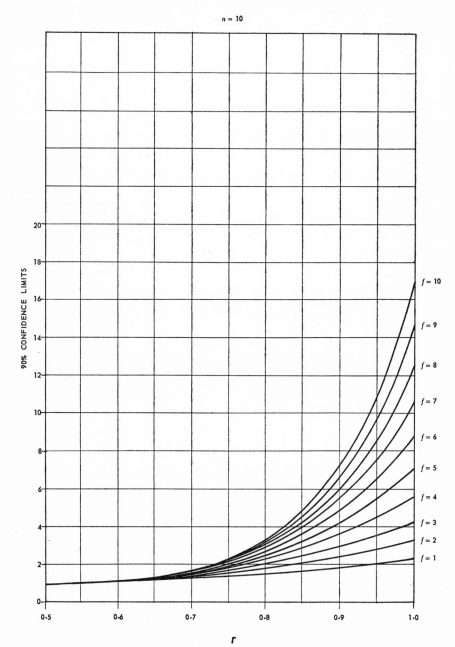

GRAPH F7 – 90% CONFIDENCE LIMITS OF MODIFIED EXPONENTIAL

$n = 11$

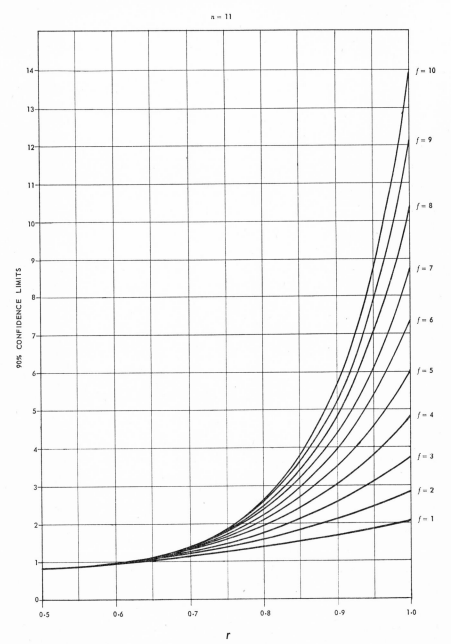

GRAPH F8 – 90% CONFIDENCE LIMITS OF MODIFIED EXPONENTIAL

$n = 12$

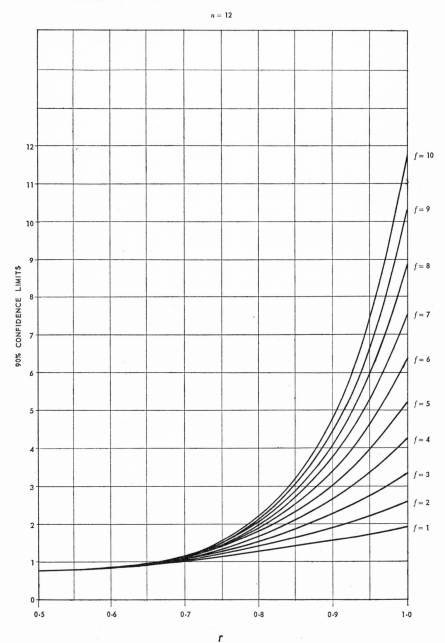

GRAPH F9 – 90% CONFIDENCE LIMITS OF MODIFIED EXPONENTIAL

$n = 13$

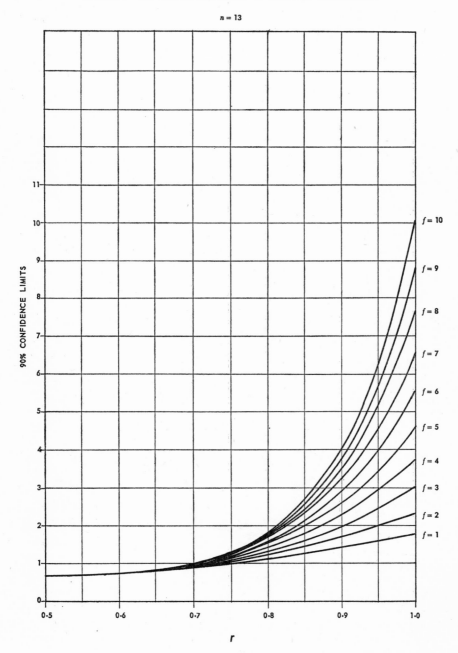

GRAPH F10 – 90% CONFIDENCE LIMITS OF MODIFIED EXPONENTIAL

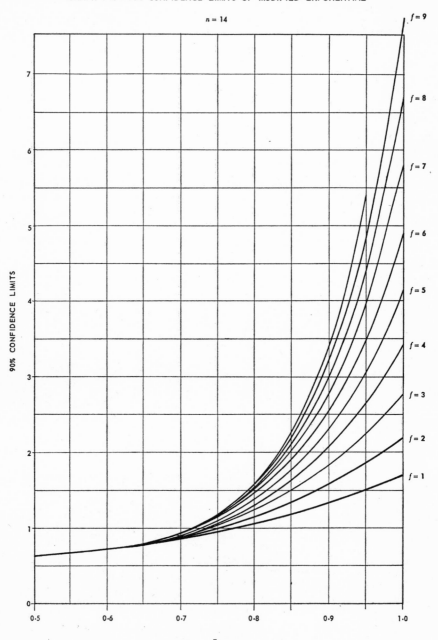

GRAPH F11 – 90% CONFIDENCE LIMITS OF MODIFIED EXPONENTIAL

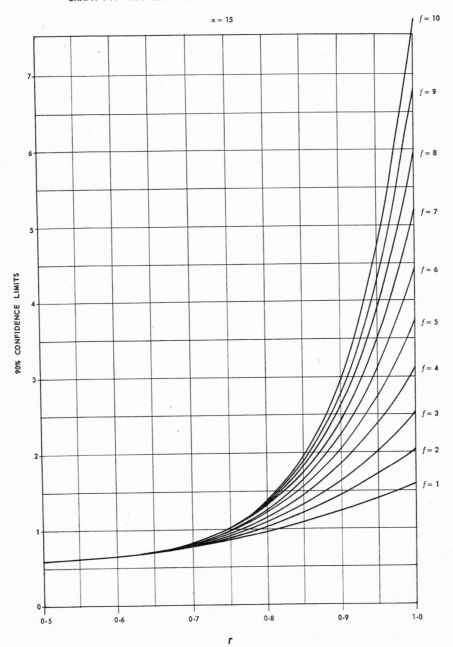

SOCIAL SCIENCE LIBRARY

Manor Road Building
Manor Road
Oxford OX1 3UQ
Tel: (2)71093 (enquiries and renewals)
http://www.ssl.ox.ac.uk

WITHDRAWN
This is a NORMAL LOAN item.

We will email you a reminder before this item is due.

Please see http://www.ssl.ox.ac.uk/lending.html
for details on:

- loan policies; these are also displayed on the
  notice boards and in our library guide.

- how to check when your books are due back.

- how to renew your books, including information
  on the maximum number of renewals.
  Items may be renewed if not reserved by
  another reader. Items must be renewed before
  the library closes on the due date.

- level of fines; fines are charged on overdue books.

Please note that this item may be recalled during Term.

WITHDRAWN

302552568-